Federico Villalba's Texas

Federico Villalba
1858-1933

Federico Villalba's TEXAS

A Mexican Pioneer's Life in the Big Bend

by
Juan Manuel Casas

IRON MOUNTAIN PRESS
Houston, Texas
2008

First Printing
June 2008

ISBN 0-9745048-5-8 (Cloth bound)
ISBN 0-9745048-6-6 (Trade paper)

Printed and Bound in the United States of America

Graphic Design by Vast Graphics, Alpine, Texas

All photographs are from the personal collection of the author except the following, courtesy of the Archives of the Big Bend, Bryan Wildenthal Memorial Library, Sul Ross State University, Alpine, Texas:

p.12: *Howard Perry on Terlingua porch, from the W. D. Smithers collection.*

p.15: *Howard Perry's Terlingua house, from the W. D. Smithers collection.*

p.47: *Smuggling sotol across the Rio Grande, from the W. D. Smithers collection.*

p.121: *Chisos Company Store, from the Casey collection.*

p.203: *Brewster County Jail, from the Casey collection.*

IRON MOUNTAIN PRESS
Houston, Texas
www.ironmtnpress.com

I dedicate this book to my mother
Herminia Villalba-Esquivel de Casas.
Her grandfather's spirit lives in her.

Map of the Big Bend of Texas (illustrated by Sandra A. Hernandez)

FOREWORD

The Big Bend area of Texas has always been an area of great drama, turmoil and change. On the surface and to the untrained eye, the feeling that "nothing happens" out in this isolated expanse of the Chihuahuan desert lures people into believing that they are totally alone and setting foot on a land that no other human has discovered.

Contrary to this feeling, historical records indicate that Álvar Núñez Cabeza de Vaca entered this vast and majestic region around 1532, some 40 years after Cristóbal Colón (Christopher Columbus) discovered the New World. Different Spanish expeditions through and around the area encountered roaming Comanche, Mescalero Apache and Chisos Indian tribes that had inhabited the region for centuries prior to the Spaniard's arrival. The nomadic nature of these early occupants who did not establish permanent communities gave the Spanish conquistador the perception that the area was "*despoblado*," uninhabited land.

The Spanish northward migration from Mexico City led to the settling of many outpost missions in the desolate desert throughout some 320 years of exploration. In the 1700s and 1800s the gradual occupation of lands by both the United States and Mexico was well developed. In 1848 with the treaty of Guadalupe Hidalgo between Mexico and the United States, the *Río Bravo del Norte* (Río Grande) in *Tejas* (Texas) was established as the border between these two nations.

It is within this geographical and chronological backdrop that Juan Manuel Casas recounts, with masterful skill, the true story of his great-grandfather, Federico Villalba.

This anecdotal history which Casas has crafted both from written documents and oral interviews with Villalba and other pioneer family members brings into focus a period of time and the fates of people who passed through the expansive vistas and deep canyons, of the area we call the Big Bend. This genealogical study is laced with raw emotion that enthralls and compels us to understand the day-to-day living of the Villalba family. Casas brings to us the joy of births, weddings and family gatherings. He shows us the victories of financial conquests and the devastation of a gunslinging society. He is able to present to us the sadness of illness and loss of life. Casas shows how Federico Villalba lived, survived and even thrived in a turbulent era of the Wild, Wild West that is the Big Bend of Texas.

Leo G. Dominguez
Associate Vice President for Advancement
Sul Ross State University, Alpine, Texas

AUTHOR'S NOTE

In writing this family history, I've used the facts of the major events in my family's story as they were passed down orally and in writing. I've woven these facts into a narrative that I hope conveys what the people in my family were thinking and feeling when these events occurred.

Some people will say how can you know what so-and-so was thinking and feeling at such-and-such a time? In some cases, the thinking and feeling was a part of the stories that were passed down. At other times, I have looked into my own heart to try to interpret the events from my family's perspective. In the case of the murder trial of Jorge Villalba, and other scenes in the book, I have reconstructed them as they might have transpired, "recreating" them based on facts and opinions that have been passed down in family history and recounted in other books and papers. Whatever liberties I've taken have been to serve the flow of the story, in the hope that the reader will be able to see and feel a violent and troubled time in Southwestern history, and yet a time that also brought out the best in people. I've never consciously distorted basic facts regarding members of Federico's family and what they did in dealing with the good and bad events that transpired during their time in the Big Bend.

My family history is also based on extensive written and oral accounts of events offered by other authors, historians and even my own family members. Sometimes what they compiled differs from what I've written. During my research, I discovered that much that has been published was erroneous to some degree. In the case of familiar accounts, I found that oftentimes stories were slanted to make a close family member the protagonist or hero of a story in contradiction to verified accounts. I have tried to recount important factual events on the basis of what I've found by way of interviews, other texts and my family's oral history. Most important facts have been confirmed by two or more independent sources or are based on forensic evidence.

I would like readers to approach this book with the understanding that family histories, when presented seriously and objectively, can enrich and expand our knowledge of times past. I hope the story of Federico Villalba's family gives people a new and fresh perspective on what life was like in the Big Bend during frontier times.

INTRODUCTION

My maternal family's odyssey in México began with the arrival of Lt. Gen. Juan de Villalba. Commissioned by King Carlos III of Spain as a military attaché, Juan came to México for the first time in 1767 with the Marqués de Rubí expedition to represent and further Spain's interests in *Nueva España* (New Spain). Juan was charged with inspecting the northern frontier of Chihuahua and making recommendations for reform to meet Spain's defensive needs. Upon returning to Spain and reporting the political unrest, King Carlos asked Juan to return to México where he would face the unenviable task of sustaining a military vigilance in a political climate that was increasingly hostile to Spanish occupation and rule. Ten generations of colonists had previously enjoyed three centuries of relative peace.

Juan and his family settled in a Spanish colony in San Geronimo in the Spanish province of Nueva Vizcaya.

Much of colonial society had tired of Spain's unrelenting, extreme self-interest and heavy taxation. At the same time, political tumult in Europe began to shake Spain. The idea behind the French and American revolutions had spread to the Americas. The seed for social and political unrest had been sown. The fruit that would grow from that seed was México's quest for independence.

Meanwhile, post 1821 Mexican settlers along Río Bravo del Norte were easy prey for Comanche war parties. These Native Americans cared little about political struggles. All they knew was that the *Comanchería* was being taken from them by intruders. Chihuahua State was a favorite target for these fierce raiders. The Mexican government acknowledged the need to do something. It dispatched a contingent of twenty-three soldiers led by Alférez (Sub-lieutenant) Mauricio Ugarte to the Chihuahua Mountains forty miles downriver from Presidio del Norte. There they were to reoccupy the old Spanish presidio along the San Carlos Arroyo and to make peace with the Comanche tribes of the region. By some miracle, Ugarte was able to hammer out a peace agreement that would keep uprisings to a minimum for much of the rest of the 19th century.

With the Comanches in check, México now had to deal with the Apaches. The Apaches were also embittered by the memory of Spanish slave traders hunting down captives to serve as labor in the silver mines of Chihuahua in northern México. The Apache, in turn, raided Spanish settlements to seize cattle, horses, firearms, and captives of their own. México encouraged citizens to create agricultural colonies along the *frontera* by offering land grants with the understanding they would work the land, raise horses and mules for war. They were to be armed and be ready to fight.

By 1880, most of the Apache bands had been driven out of West Texas by the Comanches. San Carlos ranchers took advantage of the lush grasslands on both sides of the Río Grande. Absent the threat of attack beyond the riverbanks to the north, several established Mexican ranchers decided to extend their land holdings and move their families and headquarters to Texas. Martín Solís, the largest of the ranchers, was the first to move into the Big Bend in 1879. Shortly after, other prominent Mexican ranchers followed. One of them was Federico Villalba of Aldama, Chihuahua, who set out for the Big Bend in 1880. With the ranchers came *vaqueros* and their families. Combined, they represented the first wave of Mexican immigration into the Big Bend. A second and larger wave came when the mining industry flourished in the mid to late-1890s.

Brewster County, the largest Texas county, was home to the greatest majority of the mines. Mexicans, and the few Anglo-Americans who had ventured that far south, co-existed without serious problems until new roads were built in the 1890's into the previously inaccessible Texas wilderness. These new roads and the railroad brought opportunists and land grabbers into the area.

Rancher and entrepreneur Federico Villalba fought hard to grow his land, mercantile businesses and mining interests. It was a violent time. Race alone was the cause of much violence and hostility. The early Big Bend was a dangerous land. Men carried guns and used them, in defense of their homes, their land and their honor. It was especially dangerous for people of Mexican heritage who had to surmount the prejudices and hatred of many Anglos. This is Federico Villalba's story.

1

Leaving México for the Big Bend

Federico Villalba was a restless young man, not of a mind to settle down, at least not in Aldama. From the time he was a teenager, he'd made it clear that his future was not in the old mission village north of Ciudad Chihuahua, formerly called San Geronimo. The Villalbas were of a noble Spanish blood. It appeared that the family lived a life of privilege. They were owners of the largest mercantile operation in the city and wealthy landowners, an enviable position to be in, by most standards. There was one very glaring negative aspect, however; they were *criollos*. In the Spanish colonial *castas* (caste system), a *criollo* was a person born in the Spanish colonies deemed to have *"pureza de sangre"* (purity of blood) with respect to the individual's European ancestry. The Villalbas did not prescribe to any tenet of superiority. Their light skin, eyes of color and wealth, however, were constant reminders of their origins. Feared by some, resented by others, the Villalbas, like other *criollos* were vestiges of Spanish rule. They were regarded as just so much rotting flesh on a carcass long dead.

Born in 1856, Ramón, two years Federico's senior, had made it clear that he also wanted no part of remaining in Aldama. This meant Federico was next in the line of succession. Federico, like his older and younger brothers, Arcario and Paz, and his sister, Librada wanted out from behind the looking glass. It was time for change.

Having bid farewell to Ramón, Jr., who had left for Ciudad Chihuahua to work on his cousin's ranch, Ramón Sr. pleaded for Federico to stay and manage the family ranch. But the mining of silver ore to the north and the stories of fertile ranch land along the Río Bravo del Norte were too enticing for Federico.

Federico was a handsome man with striking blue eyes. Most men in their mid-twenties were already engaged or married, in most cases by arrangement. Federico would have none of that. He would choose his spouse. He planned to marry and have a family when he could offer a wife and children stability. By his way of thinking, that wasn't anytime soon and by no means in Aldama. His imagination and his heart were set on having his own land, and, more importantly, on controlling his destiny.

In 1882, on his twenty-fourth birthday, with a land grant arranged by his father, Federico said goodbye to his parents and four siblings. With a dream of a better life, he set off on his journey north, riding his favorite horse and trailing two mules laden with supplies.

It would take one month and several close calls with Comanche braves for Federico to navigate the Chihuahuan Mountains and the harsh desert before arriving at the lower reaches of the Río Bravo del Norte near San Carlos Arroyo. A palette of yellows, browns and greens painted against a blue sky, the likes of which he'd never seen before, greeted him. The land smelled of animal rubbed into scrub brush mixed with the dank odor of reed drenched by the Río Bravo to the north. Its beauty was incomparable, yet stark. With his land grant of 100 hectares, the equivalent of 247 acres and the 5,000 pesos he had saved, Federico developed a horse and cattle ranch. He supplied stallions and beef to the Mexican Army and eventually to the U.S. Cavalry in Fort Davis, more than 100 miles to the north. The 8th Cavalry came to Fort Davis in 1875 to protect settlers and ranchers from hostile Indians roaming the border area.

Federico prospered in San Carlos, eventually tripling his land-holdings and livestock before deciding to move his operation across the Río Bravo del Norte to new country where the river was called the Río Grande.

Indian lore had it that the Great Spirit shaped the Earth, placed the stars in the heavens, the fish in the sea, and the birds in the sky and with the large pile of unused materials left over created the area that was later called the Big Bend, a mixture of rugged mountains and harsh desert, a land of enchanting beauty. One adventurer described the desert's plants as "porcupines, armed to the teeth." The Spanish called the Southwest desert *"El Despoblado,"* the uninhabited land. Human presence was unnatural therein.

In Texas, Federico laid claim to 10,240 acres in the central Burro Mesa area and 10,000 acres along the west side of the Chisos Mountains.

In the distance loomed the Santa Elena Canyon, an area that is quite possibly one of the most strikingly beautiful locations in North America. The canyons most beautiful aspect was also its most treacherous. Carved out of limestone originally deposited as sediment by the ocean that once covered the Big Bend millions of years ago, the canyon, narrow and sheer, reaches up 1,500 feet above the river in some places.

Federico's herd of cattle had grown from a few hundred head when he first crossed the Río Grande to more than 2,000 between his ranch in San Carlos and Burro Mesa. His brand was the letter A, which in ancient times symbolized the "great white bull," Alba. The brand would become well known in the region.

Rancho Barras brand

Federico named his spread Rancho Barras after his great-grandmother, Celestine Barras de Villalba, the wife of Juan. Born of French nobility, Celestine left a comfortable life in Spain to accompany her husband to a hostile land. Over the years, Federico heard stories of her strength and abiding faith in her husband. He hoped that by christening his land with his great-grandmother's family name his land would be faithful to him.

West Texas desert

Change came in a big way to the Big Bend in 1884. Word quickly spread of the discovery of cinnabar, a mercury-bearing ore. The bright red substance the Spanish called *asoge* (pronounced ah-so-ghe) was used by Native Americans as war paint and as pigment for rock paintings. There are many more documented uses of mercury or quicksilver as it is also called, going back to Ancient Greece. Over the centuries its applications included cosmetics and for medicinal purposes, contraception and treatment of syphilis; the malevolent used it as poison. In 1799, Edward Charles Howard perfected a process using mercury as a detonator. The product, called mercuric fulminate, is used in blasting caps to detonate dynamite and as percussion devices in bombs. The search for gold and man's inability to peacefully cohabit this Earth created the greatest demand for the mineral during the zenith of the mining activities of the Big Bend. Federico, to his gratification, discovered the versatile ore on his land along the Chisos. For the next few years, Federico's men would glean surface outcroppings with pick and shovel for deposits. Surface prospecting for quicksilver, however, began to yield less and less. It soon became necessary to dig deeper.

Federico Finds a Bride

Between the leather goods operation and his cattle ranch, Federico decided it was time to build and stock a store, which he did in *Cerro Villalba*. The store was simply called *La Tiendita*, the little store. It stocked farm utensils, sundry supplies and a few canned goods. Because perishables wouldn't keep long, the store only stocked as much as could be sold or used in a week. The store always smelled of onions and jalapeño chiles, staples of most Mexican diets. The good thing is they kept longer than most other perishables. As more and more families moved into the region, the store began carrying fabrics, mostly the sort that appealed to Federico. That changed when he hired the wife of one of his *vaqueros* to help tend the store. She told him that most of the fabric he carried was more appropriate for horse blankets than for people. It was her way of saying the store lacked a woman's touch.

It made Federico think. Maybe it was time for a change in his life. Having launched three successful businesses by age 30, Federico now felt ready for marriage. He frequently traveled to Fort Davis on business. On one of his trips, he happened on a young lady named María, the daughter of his supplier of *aceite de comer*, olive oil. Sixteen-year-old María and her 20-year-old brother, Maximiliano, were the children of Ruperto and Jesusita Navarette de Cortez.

The day María met Federico, she and her brother were helping their father tend to the store. María had a beautiful smile and glowing skin. Though she was small, her personality filled the room. Federico was instantly smitten, though the same can't be said for María. Fourteen years her senior, Federico was, by her standards, an old man. He was handsome enough, but she would tell her father, "*Está muy viejo*, he's too old." Federico's biggest ally in helping win María over was her father. Ruperto had brought his family up from Allende, México, in 1885, first to Alpine and then to Fort Davis. He grew to like and respect Federico.

On a reciprocal visit to Terlingua, once he saw the extent of Federico's holdings, Ruperto became convinced that Federico could give his daughter a good life, despite the age difference. On May 17, 1889, Federico married María and took her to *Cerro* Villalba where he had built a small, one bedroom house near his store. Not one to rush into things, he waited four years to bring a child into the world. On April 16, 1893, they had their first child, a boy they named Felipe. Two years later Jorge was born. As she had done with Felipe, María returned to Fort Davis to deliver her second child, where she and her baby could receive proper medical attention should there be complications a midwife could not handle.

In 1898, María's parents retired and returned to Allende, México. Shortly thereafter, María's brother Max concluded that the family store would do better in Marfa, Texas, the Presidio County seat, about 21 miles southwest of Fort Davis. Seven years earlier, the Army had closed the fort, reassigning troops elsewhere. Business was at an all-time low. After Max moved the store to Marfa, Federico bought a home there not far from Max's adobe. He wanted María to have a place to stay whenever she visited her brother. It would also be a place to birth any future children.

In September, the Marfa home was filled with the cries of a beautiful baby girl. They named her Regina. Regina was the biggest baby yet, weighing nearly 10 pounds at birth.

María had followed her heart to *Cerro* Villalba. She was a strong woman who took most things in stride. Federico had done everything possible to make her comfortable, but now they had three children to consider. With the newest arrival, María began talking of a bigger home. It was she who suggested they live at the ranch, and Federico began to build a real home on Rancho Barras in Burro Mesa that winter. Federico's dream of a family and economic security was now a reality. He was 39 years old and one of the most successful ranchers and businessmen in the Big Bend.

The Marfa and Mariposa Mining Company opened the first large commercial cinnabar venture in the Big Bend in 1898. The site of the mine became known as California Hill about four and one-half mile west of Terlingua.

In 1899, Martín Solís, Federico's good friend, discovered the precious ore near his property. He launched mining operations in the Maríscal Mountains. Though cinnabar was plentiful, the difficulty from the onset lay in transporting it more than 30 miles by mule to Terlingua. The original town of Terlingua was a small Mexican village located along Terlingua Creek three miles above its convergence with the Río Grande. The name Terlingua is said to be a derivation of the words *tres lenguas*, meaning three tongues, either referring to the three forks of the creek or the three languages spoken by the Comanche, Apache and Shawnee Indians whose villages at one time were spread over 83 miles of the creek's banks.

Ed Lindsay, a U.S. Customs official, postmaster and mine and store owner in Boquillas, a small village on the Río Grande, finally decided the cost of running his Lindsay Mine, 30 miles southeast of Terlingua, was too difficult. He sold his operations to Isaac Sanger of Dallas, who changed the name to the Texas Almaden Mining Company.

Federico Discovers Mercury

In 1902, Federico entered into a partnership with a local doctor by the name of Will Study (pronounced Stoody) and Tiburcio de la Rosa. The mining claim was filed by Study, and in subsequent partnership documents, Federico and Tiburcio were described as "original discovers." Each man owned one-third interest with Study slated to be the financier for the operation. The partnership covered six parcels at twenty-one acres each originally owned by H.E. & W.J. Railway Company. Combined, these claims comprised the nucleus of the Big Bend Mining Company operations in what was known as *Cerro* Villalba.

Adjunct to the partnership agreement, Federico and Tiburcio signed one-third of their individual interests along with a power of attorney to D. Alarcón for $2.00. This translated to Will Study retaining one entire third interest in the operation while Federico, Tiburcio and Alarcón split the remaining two-thirds. From then on *Cerro* Villalba became known as Study Butte, the mine, the Study Butte Mine and Federico's store; you guessed it, the Study Butte store.

Within two months of establishing the partnership, the men entered into a new agreement with another group of miners, Ed Gleim and his brothers George and H. W., Morris Kirk and Spencer Gregg. The group paid $100.00 for a one-year option to purchase the mining claim for $30,000.00. Of that sum, Will Study was to receive $10,000.00 with Federico, Tiburcio and Alarcón receiving $6,656.66 each, along with 2% stock in the resulting mining company. In June of the following year, the Gleim group exercised their option.

Business Rivalries
in the Big Bend

By 1905, the Big Bend Quicksilver Mine and the Texas Almaden Mining Company, both located in Study Butte, and the newly developed Chisos Mining Company in Terlingua began luring silver miners and their families from Coahuila, San Carlos and Santa Eulalia in México with the prospect of making twice the pay. As luck would have it, Villalba's store now also served the miners of Study Butte. The store, relocated to a larger adobe building Federico bought a year earlier, was renamed the Study Butte Store.

Study Butte Store in the 1950s

Federico's mercantile business prospered and his store expanded. Federico also had become the foremost supplier of Mexican leather goods to the Anglo ranchers in the area. The majority of the cowboys were Mexican. The *vaqueros* much preferred the considerably larger horn of the Mexican saddle. The quality of the lariats, bridles, chaps and bullwhips that Federico supplied was unsurpassed. Eventually, he would monopolize the importation of these products by promising his Mexican suppliers he would buy everything they made. This way, he could ensure that little or no leather goods would be sold to his Anglo competitors.

Howard Perry

Federico's success with Rancho Barras, his involvement in mining and his Study Butte store and leather goods business made him a leading business figure in the area. One man who took notice of Federico was Howard Perry, the owner of the Chisos Mining Company and the Chisos Store. Perry, a shrewd Chicago industrialist, had acquired the property that was later developed as the Chisos Mine in the late 1880s. Though details of his purchase are still debated, the legal maneuvers by which he wrested control of the richest part of the property from R. C. McKinney, T. D. McKinney and J. M. Parker, who had previously filed mining claims on the same property, are well documented. With an assist from Austin attorney Eugene Cartledge, Perry was granted a court order prohibiting the McKinneys and Parker from continuing operations on the property. His assertions that boundaries had been assigned erroneously by Brewster County surveyor William M. Harmon and, previous to that John T. Gano, were upheld by the court.

Perry began developing the mine, and he quickly became known for his harsh treatment of Mexican employees, who comprised nearly ninety percent of his workforce. Perry had a slave-owner mentality, underpaying and overworking his employees. This circumstance did not go unnoticed or without strong and open criticism by Federico. He made it well known that he thought

Howard Perry on Terlingua Porch

Perry was *"un hombre sin consiencia,* a man without a conscience." This little man from the Midwest might be intimidating to his employees and others in the region, but he bore no weight on Federico. Federico, as did other Mexican residents, began referring to Perry as *"El Perro,* the dog."

By 1906, the United States economy had taken a dramatic downturn. The financial panic that followed in 1907 resulted in a recession. The Mexican economy, with close ties to the American economy, also faltered. Thousands of Mexicans who worked in the United States lost their jobs and upon returning to México found its economy also in shambles. Many moved to the Big Bend where word had it that jobs in the mines, ranches and farms were plentiful. It came as no surprise to Federico that the Chisos Mine took advantage of the surplus of workers, offering them one-third of the salary for similar work in other areas of the United States. Grateful for any work, Mexicans took the jobs. Perry became a millionaire on the backs of his predominantly Mexican employees.

After the initial push of opening the mine, Perry soon began spending most of his time at his mansion in Portland, Maine. He visited the Big Bend only two or three times a year. He received daily reports by letter or telegram from the mine's superintendent. The first superintendent was Dr. William Battle Phillips, a noted Texas mining engineer and geologist. To accommodate his short stays in Terlingua, Perry would eventually build a large home on a hill overlooking the town.

Some people said it was his way of sending townspeople a message. Even though he was not always there physically, his influence was ever present.

Villalba Family Photo (circa 1906)
An unidentified neighbor girl is seated in Federico's lap. Seated in the highchair
is Federico, next to him in the chair is Jacobo. Standing to Maria's left is Regina,
next to her is Jorge. The eldest son Felipe is not shown.

In Boquillas, trouble was brewing for Martín Solís. His son, Benito, was a suspect in the murder of Max Ernst, a German immigrant who lived in La Noria, eight miles northwest of Boquillas. Ernst was a rancher, notary public, justice of the peace and county commissioner. He had also opened a small schoolhouse in La Noria. The chain of events that led to Ernst's death began when Ed Lindsay, who had been postmaster since 1896, sold his store in Boquillas and moved to Lajitas in 1900. Solís saw Ernst's absence as an opportunity to open his own store and assume the unofficial role of postmaster. He hoped to be appointed postmaster in due time. In the meantime, Jesse Deemer opened a store to compete with Solís, with the backing of C. W. Hess, a Marathon retailer. Ernst was busy currying favor with the local big wigs, lobbying to have himself appointed postmaster, and he succeeded. In 1901, the U.S. post office was relocated to La Noria. One year later, Ernst opened the Big Tinaja Store in Boquillas and moved the post office

Howard Perry's house in Terlingua

View of the Chisos Mountains

with him, though he did not formally apply for permission to do so until 1903. It is generally believed that his manipulations were his undoing. Ernst's store meant major competition for Solís's operation, not to mention the animosity that existed from Ernst having been appointed postmaster.

On September 27, 1908, Ernst was shot three times while rounding a blind bend on horseback on his way into Boquillas. It was said that Ernst penned a note as he lay dying suggesting that a Solís had shot him. Several members of the Solís family, including Martín's son, Benito, who ran the family store, were suspects. The Brewster County Grand Jury charged Francisco, Juan, Tomás, Benito and Martín and seven others for the murder on a complaint filed by Ernst's wife, Rosa. On March 18, 1909, the charges were dismissed for lack of evidence. No one was ever prosecuted for the murder. Due perhaps to the persistent rumors about his role in Ernst's death, Benito Solís eventually sold the store and moved away. The violent death was one of many to come, as one of the last frontier areas attracted more settlers. It was the waning days of the old West, but violence and gunplay could erupt at any time, as Federico's family was soon to learn.

Revolution Comes to the Big Bend

Over the next two years, the dynamics of the Big Bend began shifting due in great part to the political infighting taking place in México between *Presidente* Porfirio Díaz and dissident Francisco Madero. The Big Bend was reputed to be the wildest and most unruly part of Texas. Area ranchers were recruited by Texas Rangers to help protect land along the Río Grande. Given warrants of authority and special commissions to investigate crimes against the United States and its citizens, the men who were commissioned were given free reign to render justice on the spot. In 1909, Federico was approached by the sheriff who encouraged him to accept a commission. Federico did so for one big reason. He didn't much care for Pancho Villa. It offered the American government's protection if he or any of his *vaqueros* killed an interloping Villa sympathizer.

Francisco Madero was imprisoned in 1910 as an insurgent at Porfirio Díaz's direction. It was a disastrous attempt to assure Díaz's election. A plot to overthrow Díaz was immediately hatched behind bars by Madero. Hostilities began spreading. The swell of unrest began in Puebla, México, and surged northward.

Terlingua soon felt the effects of the revolution. Tagged as *bandidos* by the Anglos, revolutionaries raided settlements and ranches across the Río Grande, in search of horses, guns and ammunition they could use in the war. As far back as 1908, Perry had feared that the lonely outpost of Terlingua was a plum just waiting to be picked by *bandidos*. Though he professed to be worried for the citizenry, his sole concern was for his money and mine. The next invasion the Big Bend finally experienced was not by *bandidos*, but by Mexican refugees who crossed the river to flee the violence and insecurity in their homeland. By the middle of January 1911, 300 or so immigrants were camped out on Chisos Mine property. By March, the number had climbed to more than 400. The refugees looked for work, but it was either unavailable or withheld. Those who found work were employed at substandard wages. Living in caves or *jacales*, wattle and daub huts, refugees found themselves in extremely oppressive and impoverished conditions. Resident Mexican families offered immigrants what little nourishment and water they could spare. Smoldering campfires and the stench of human excrement hovered over the area.

The Chisos Mine management was not concerned about offering help or improving inhumane conditions. They only offered more heartache. Perry was convinced that his workers and the newly arrived refugees were revolutionary sympathizers. Equally certain that they were plotting against him, Perry wrote a letter to Brig. Gen. Joseph W. Duncan at Fort Sam Houston advising him of the situation in Terlingua. Perry requested the general send "a small company of soldiers" to deal with the "sympathizers." He laced the communication with scenarios of intercepting wagon trains, which were carrying Mexicans across the border in such numbers that his "property which had taken hundreds of thousands of dollars to create would have to be abandoned." It was simple. Perry wanted the refugees gone. He would paint as grim a picture as he could to convince the military to drive the Mexicans back across the river.

It was true that Perry's employees openly discussed the revolution and who was best for the mother country, Madero or Díaz, but there was never any thought of biting the hand that fed them. As for the newly arrived immigrants, they had fled the violence of México; there was no desire on their part to import it to Texas. Perry closed his letter with an appeal to Duncan that he keep his request "confidential". His reasoning was that he didn't want word to get back to his employees. He wrote, "They, as a class, are a suspicious people and might not understand."

In truth, his desire for secrecy had to do with the merchants in Alpine and Marfa, where the troops were now stationed. The merchants would certainly oppose any troop movements. It would mean losing their protectors, not to mention a substantial source of revenue. By whatever indifference or opposition, Perry's request fell on deaf ears. Perry was disappointed but not derailed. In the succeeding months, he proceeded to pen letters to top military leaders, including the Army chief of staff, asking for help. He wrote to the secretary of war and a multitude of congressmen and senators.

In the meantime, Madero was either released or escaped from prison, there are differing accounts, and fled to Texas where he plotted the overthrow of Díaz. The thirty-one year dictatorship of México's President Díaz came to an end with the defeat of Díaz's army in Ciudad Juárez in March, 1911. Díaz resigned on May 11, 1911.

Tragically, the political changeover failed to bring peace. Pascual Orozco, a former commander in Madero's revolutionary army, under whom Pancho Villa had served, felt slighted that he was not promised his rightful place in the new government. He immediately started a counterrevolution. Pancho Villa, in the meantime, had married and left for Ciudad Chihuahua, to make a new life with his bride, Luz. His retirement was short-lived. On January 31, 1912, the Juárez military garrison revolted. President Madero asked Villa to help spearhead a renewed effort to bring peace to México. Villa complied. He recruited troops and rode under the command of Gen. Victoriano Huerta in support of Madero. Upon Villa's arrival, Huerta was overwhelmed by Villa's popularity. It became readily apparent that Villa was held in much higher regard than he. Fearing that his popularity might give Villa ideas about wrenching command from him, Huerta had Villa arrested in 1912 for insubordination, and of all things, for stealing a horse. Villa was summarily sentenced to death. Madero, hearing of Villa's plight, ordered Pancho's reprieve only minutes from his execution. Villa was spared, though Huerta kept him imprisoned. By the time Villa escaped prison in December 1912, Huerta had switched from being a Madero supporter to an adversary.

Tensions along the border increased. On February 9, 1912, a large contingent of *revolucionarios* demanded the surrender of Presidio, some 50 miles from Terlingua. The ongoing political instability in México was eventually seen as a threat to American security. Thanks to Texas Gov. O. B. Colquitt and a letter he wrote to Gen. Duncan requesting protection from the "hostile Mexican element," Perry finally had his way, to a degree. In February, an eight-man detachment was dispatched to Terlingua. Perry considered it a "token gesture."

On February 22, 1913, *huertistas* assassinated Madero and claimed the presidency for their leader. This gave Perry fresh ammunition to step up his demand for a larger military presence. Still, he could not convince the local authorities of an increased threat. Perry was probably most anxious about the support Villa was enjoying on the Texas side.

Villa's brother, Hipólito, in concert with Toribio Ortega and Albino Aranda was purchasing guns and supplies in large numbers from U.S. merchants. Candelaria and Presidio were known as Villa towns. It is said that at one time, as many as 30 people in the Big Bend area supplied guns to Villa's army. Unbeknownst to Federico, his older brother, Ramón, who lived in Cd. Chihuahua, had become a confederate of Villa's and one of those supplying him with arms.

In 1915, Perry set out for Washington. He began his campaign in the House of Representatives and then moved to the Senate. With the help of Maine Sen. Charles Fletcher Johnson, he also met with Secretary of War Lindley M. Garrison. His appeal to the secretary was ostensibly based on his fear for the safety of "our white women and little children." It was a thin veil for his real reason, which he made abundantly clear to the secretary in a letter following their meeting. In the letter, he cleverly pointed out the value of the continued production of mercury for any war effort. His underlying point was that, in and of themselves, the mines of Terlingua merited increased protection. Though it was blatantly apparent that his letter was self-serving, his allusion to the value of mercury was unquestionable. By way of some additional political maneuvering, Perry secured Secretary Garrison's consent to set in motion a plan to send additional troops to Terlingua. On October 19, 1915, Troop A of the 13th Cavalry received orders to transfer from Alpine to Terlingua. Though it was confidential, word leaked of the troop movement. Alpine merchants and the troop's commander immediately started a letter writing campaign to have the order reversed.

But, Perry had done a masterful job of bamboozling the political hierarchy. The transfer was completed in November. The move was doomed from the very beginning. What had been passed off as good for the community, turned into a debacle of the first order. Having taken the lead from their commander, the soldiers had great resentment for the people of Terlingua, fixating mostly on the Mexican residents.

Protect Us from Our Saviors

Soon after the troops arrived in Terlingua, a disgraceful incident occurred that even drew the ire of the Chisos Mine's general manager, Wayne Cartledge. The morning of December 1, 1915, was opening day for deer hunting season. An avid hunter, Wayne Cartledge and some of his friends had left before daylight for a day of camaraderie, and, hopefully, some trophies. The previous day had been payday for Troop A. Some of the men had celebrated with an all-night drinking binge and a poker party in town. At dawn, as they walked to their quarters, the soldiers spotted several Mexican children driving a herd of goats near the Cartledge home. One of the men convinced the others to use the goats as target practice. They didn't stop shooting until every goat was dead. Miraculously, the children escaped the gunfire.

Mrs. Cartledge, who was awake and in the kitchen after seeing her husband off, frantically slipped out of her home and fled to safer surroundings. When Wayne returned home later that evening, his wife described what had happened. He immediately called the commanding officer in Marfa and demanded disciplinary action. An officer was sent to assess the incident. He was unmoved by Cartledge's account of the event and the fifteen goat carcasses presented for his examination. When told that the owner of the goats wanted $2.50 for every animal that had been killed, the officer stormed out of Cartledge's office shouting, "Send them goddamned savages back to Mexico."

The culprits were never punished, and the owner of the goats was never paid for his loss.

In another even more tragic incident, Mariano Mireles, a young father of three, was murdered by several soldiers. Mariano was playing cards and had won several hands when one soldier accused him of cheating. Believing the accuser, the others became incensed. One suddenly pulled a knife and began stabbing Mariano. When it was all over, Mariano had been stabbed repeatedly in the face and chest by more than one man.

Instead of assuming the role of protectors, the troopers turned into a lawless band of marauders. The military brass quickly realized that they had been duped into believing that Terlingua was in peril from Mexican revolutionaries. Ironically, their biggest challenge to date had been to keep disgruntled U.S. soldiers from meting out the very devastation that had been feared of the revolutionaries. In January 1916, all but 20 of the soldiers were returned to Alpine. Indifferent to the atrocities inflicted on the Mexican citizens of Terlingua, Perry tried to convince the military that it was making a serious mistake in withdrawing the bulk of the troops.

The error of sending soldiers in the first place was indelibly and tragically inscribed in Terlingua's history, but Perry couldn't or wouldn't acknowledge the travesty. The raid led by Pancho Villa in Columbus, New Mexico, in March, 1916 and subsequent raids by Villa's troops in the Big Bend area incited additional ill-will toward Mexicans. Even so, Mexicans continued crossing the river to Texas for a better life.

Unfortunately, some also came with criminal motivation. After a raid by *bandidos* at Glenn Springs resulting in the death of three American soldiers and a child, the *Marathon Hustler*, ran an editorial on May 13, 1916 that captured popular local opinion:

> *"Men laugh and joke in the presence of death, and there is no such thing as murder. Every man would think he was honored to be detailed to fire the fatal shot that would send some raider to his death. There is an element of justice running through it all that takes away all sense of barbarism; but there are only two words in every man's mind, 'Kill and Revenge.' And heaven help the Mexican that can't show a clean record."*

Dangerous Times

For people of Mexican heritage, the following years in the Big Bend were filled with racial tension. Bolstered by the ruthlessness of a few Texas Rangers who roamed the area, Anglos felt as if they were a superior force. They were well armed and ready to fight the Mexican "*bandidos.*" In 1918, following a raid on a Presidio County ranch by a band of Mexican brigands, several Texas Rangers in pursuit entered the village of Porvenir, on the north bank of the Río Grande. There, they indiscriminately rounded up 15 poor tenant farmers, all of whom made their home on the U.S. side. The men were taken a short distance from town, lined up along a bluff, and executed in cold blood by the Rangers. From then on the Texas Rangers went from being called *"Los Rinches"*, an innocuous play on the word Rangers, to being called *"Los Diablos Tejanos,"* the Texas Devils.

Federico began to hear grumblings from his children. The *diablos'* behavior seemed to be a repeat of the military occupation of Terlingua two years earlier. The younger Villalbas were understandably upset and wanted to take revenge on the Rangers. The Big Bend was their birthplace. Alongside their father, they had worked to build and maintain the family's holdings. Up until now, Federico's detractors had been confined to Howard Perry's henchmen and the United States military, but now they had to deal with the Texas Rangers and the hatred they fomented along the border. It was becoming far too dangerous for the Villalba family. Federico realized it would be only a matter of time before he or one of his children would be confronted by an angry Anglo. The outcome would likely be fatal to the slower hand. Federico grappled with his feelings, finally contacting the sheriff to inform him he was resigning his commission in protest. He wanted nothing more to do with the Texas Rangers.

Each of Federico's children, including his daughter Regina, were well trained in firearms. They all wore side arms, and they were all crack shots. Regina could hit a dollar coin thrown in the air. Her younger brother, Santos, told a story of him and Regina riding their horses one day when a rabbit darted from the brush and across the trail, spooking the horse. The horse reared back, throwing his sister from the saddle. Regina instinctively drew her gun and, "Shot and killed the rabbit before she ever hit the ground," Santos would brag.

Fifteen-year-old Jacobo "Jake" Villalba, the most rambunctious and rebellious of Federico's children, was the first of the clan to have a run-in with an Anglo.

Delfi "Det" Walker was nine years older than Jacobo. It happened in Study Butte as Jacobo innocently walked northward towards the family store. His eyes were following a young *señorita* who had just entered the store. Jacobo failed to notice a man walking towards him. He quickened his pace in anticipation of meeting the young lady. A harsh voice suddenly tore him from his thoughts.

"Hey Mexican, you're supposed to step aside when a white man is walking your way," Walker barked.

"I walk aside for no man!" Jacobo responded. Jacobo would cower in fear for no one, much less a *"gringo"*.

Ignoring Walker's glare, Jacobo walked past the man, purposely brushing against his right arm. A telltale twitch of Walker's muscle was enough to warn Jacobo that the stranger might be going for his gun. Jacobo spun around, simultaneously unholstering his pistol.

Jacobo Villalba at age fifteen (Circa 1918)

Walker's hand was indeed gripping the butt-end of his gun, poised to draw the weapon.

Jacobo pointed the gun at Walker's heart as he spoke. "I may be young, but I'm not slow."

Walker slowly removed his hand from the pistol.

"No trouble, no trouble," he repeated, holding both hands up to his side.

Jacobo smirked boldly at Walker. "I think one of us should leave, don't you agree, *gringo?*"

Walker retreated to his horse ten paces behind never taking his eyes off Jacobo. He reached behind, fumbling blindly with the reins on the hitching post. Jacobo lowered his gun, but did not put it in his holster until Walker had mounted his horse and rode away. The encounter was a defining moment in Jacobo's life. His act of defiance became well known in the Big Bend, something that would never sit well with Det Walker and would lead to more trouble later.

2

Trusting Neighbors

Tensions continued to mount as the revolution in México persisted, sporadically spilling over into the Big Bend. Anti-Mexican sentiment was increasing, fueled by the overreaction and misguided hostility of the Texas Rangers. Federico's good friends, Roy and Hallie Stillwell, a prominent Anglo ranching family, distanced themselves from such sentiment, as did many of Federico's Anglo compatriots, but not without paying a price. The schism between Anglos and Mexicans had widened. Violence was a regular way of life on both sides of the border. Big Bend ranch hands who stood between rustlers and cattle were often killed. Livestock was driven across the Río Grande into México.

In 1917, blame was often and sometimes mistakenly laid on Cuco Torres, a notorious Mexican bandit who brazenly raided Texas ranches, oftentimes killing or wounding those who stood their ground. However, during one incident, *avisadores*, or messengers, who stood atop hills and used mirrors to flash messages in code to each other, sent word that Torres was not the responsible party. The *avisadores*, also referred to as the "Mexican Grapevine," stymied Anglos who were unable to decipher the codes.

Federico, who himself had lost cattle, relayed a message to his fellow ranchers that the cattle were being sold to Mexican ranchers across the river by Anglos. One of the culprits, identified by the mirror flashes, was a foreman who worked for one of the more vociferous of the unsympathetic ranchers. The man had made no bones about telling anyone who would listen that "anyone who defended Mexicans was no better than them thieving *bandidos.*" Nevertheless, the Stillwell's and other sympathetic ranchers' allegiances remained firmly with Federico.

Roy Stillwell had married the previous August, 1918, and brought his school-teacher bride, Hallie Crawford, to his ranch in Maravillas Canyon to begin their new life. What he presented to her was a one-room, 12 x 15-foot ranch house that they would share with Stillwell's two ranch hands.

Federico kidded Roy about this arrangement.

"You can't be making love to your new bride with an audience," he said, teasing him.

Whether by Federico's cajoling or Hallie's urging, Roy soon committed to build his young bride a "proper bedroom" before winter. As hard as Roy tried, he was unable to keep his promise, because a time of chaos and danger overtook the Big Bend during the next few months.

As World War I waned, an influenza pandemic broke out in the United States and quickly spread to Europe. The French called it "*Le Grippe,*" referring to the menacing hold it had on the country. It traveled swiftly, viciously wreaking havoc throughout the world. The wave of devastation killed thousands before reaching Fort Stockton, a sleepy ranching village about 150 miles northeast of Terlingua. In mid-October, 1918, a number of people became ill in Terlingua. It was in the deadly grasp of what was being called the

Spanish flu though there was never any proof that it originated in Spain. On October 31, 1918 Terlingua recorded its first influenza death.

Terlingua was in turmoil in the autumn of 1918. In addition to what seemed a never-ending civil war just across the Rio Grande, along with all its attendant problems, the "War to End All Wars" in Europe was winding down. Germany sued for peace, and a *rapprochement* would be gained with the signing of an armistice on November 11. Good news it was to most Americans, but probably not so fine for the capitalist Howard E. Perry and his Chisos Mining concern at Terlingua. The demand for mercury would now certainly drop, and with it the price of a flask of the liquid metal. Jobs hung in the balance.

More immediate, however, a silent killer was sliding its gruesome scythe across the Western Hemisphere. The Spanish influenza had struck the United States during October, and its airborne virus spread quickly along the railway routes that had by now spider-webbed across the continent. Mule-drawn wagonloads of mining tools, store goods, passengers and soldiery were constantly being carted from Marathon and Alpine to the Rio Grande country before re-lading with heavy flasks of quicksilver for the return trip and deliverance at the depot. And with those shipments cycled the grim reaper, a hooded visage casting a shadow none could see, but all would learn to dread.

"¡Dios mio!" I cannot afford to be sick, thought *la Señora* Maria Villalba. She remembered that it was the first day of November.

El Día de los Angelitos, All Souls Day. And tomorrow…El Día de los Muertos. There is too much to do. But when Maria attempted to raise her head or find strength to slide from beneath the blanket, there came feeble response.

Ayer, the previous day, Federico's wife had felt a chill and lightness of head; she asked her husband to arrange a bed in the kitchen so she might appreciate the warmth cast from the four-burner, mesquite-fired cook stove a night or two. *This early fall,* she thought, *is affecting me strangely.* Now she heard Federico come inside and step near.

"*Mi amor,*" she whispered. "I do not feel well."

Federico put the back of his hand to his wife's brow. What he felt was dampness, like the heavy dew on Chino grass that comes three days following a hurricane's slam into the Gulf Coast. The bed sheets were soaking; she was hot like a dropped charcoal on the desert floor, somber and grey on the outside but within, all a-rouge. *My God!* he thought and stomped over to the door where Regina slept; Federico crashed his fist against the wooden slats.

"Come to the kitchen," he barked. "Your mother is ill."

Daughter Regina slipped beneath a coverlet and came tripping into the warm kitchen. Her eyes were wide and anxious, like a startled doe.

"What is it, Papá?"

"*Es la gripa mi hija. Tengo medio.* I'm afraid. Go get your brothers. Tell Jacobo to run for *la mina* and ask Señor Cartledge to send the company doctor as quickly as he can get here."

Regina flew barefoot past the kitchen door; behind, it slammed shut with a somber thud.

If it is la gripa, thought the husband, *I'll have to send someone to telegraph Marathon and then a message to Chihuahua and on to*

Allende. Felipe must be informed, and he's three hundred miles away. God help us.

Dr. R. A. Wilson, the only doctor in Terlingua, was dispatched by Wayne Cartledge, the mine's general manager who himself was recovering from the illness he'd contracted weeks earlier. He was one of the luckier ones whose illness did not worsen to become pneumonia.

Dr. Wilson soon arrived at Rancho Barras. Shortly after, Jacobo and Jorge arrived, having been summoned by Regina. After a brief examination, the doctor turned to Federico.

"May I speak to you in the hallway?"

Federico's children followed. As soon as the doctor felt he was sufficiently out of María's earshot, he spoke.

"I'm sorry there is nothing I can do to help her at this point," he said. "All we can do is give her plenty of liquids and try and keep her fever down."

"There is no medicine you can give her?" Federico asked anxiously.

"Nothing," Dr. Wilson said. It was news he'd given distraught relatives many times over the last few weeks. Federico thanked the doctor and asked him what he owed.

"For what," Dr. Wilson answered, "I did nothing."

Federico thanked the doctor a second time as he walked him to the door. The children returned to their mother's bedside. Federico contemplated his next move as he returned to his wife. He respected Dr. Wilson, but he was not willing to settle for hopelessness.

María had fallen asleep. Federico motioned for his children to follow him to the hallway.

"We are going to México, to Allende," he said. "Perhaps there we can get your mother some help. We will leave as soon as you can prepare the car and the trucks," he told his sons.

"Regina, prepare a bed for your mother in the Model T Ford. I want to make her as comfortable as possible for the trip."

Federico took a chair from the kitchen table and sat sentry next to the bed as his wife slept and his children left to do their tasks.

María awoke briefly. Federico bent over and whispered his decision into her ear. A tiny smile emanated from her ashen face. Happy to be returning home, María knew of many who had succumbed to the illness and bore no better expectations. If she were to die, it would be in her *tierra*, homeland. She slept and dreamed of angels that promised to care for her husband and her children if she were to leave them.

Federico and his children set off for Chihuahua in the middle of the day. It would be a challenging trip for Jorge and his wife, Golla, who was five months pregnant.

Federico left his land and his businesses to some of his most trusted employees to care for. Fearing *bandidos*, Federico chose to leave his money on the United States side. He mistrusted banks, American and Mexican alike. Bank robberies in the region were frequent. Mexican banks close to the border were especially vulnerable. In those days, banks didn't guarantee deposits so Federico buried his money. Burying money may have seemed like an impractical way to secure his funds, but to Federico the odds seemed far greater that the bank would be robbed than the random chance someone would happen on his money. Vaquero, *"El Gringo Nicanor"*, one of Federico's most trusted men, was shown where his money had been secreted. Nicanor was given his moniker by Federico back when he worked for Dolores García. Dolores owned the neighboring ranch and was Federico's best friend. Nicanor was *güero*, light complexioned. He had been mistaken for Anglo many times. He liked his nickname and he wore it like a badge of honor. If you were christened with a nickname by Federico, it meant you were special to him. That counted for a lot. Nicanor would accompany the Villalbas to México. The plan was for Nicanor to return to the Big Bend whenever it was necessary to make deposits or withdrawals from the Bank of Villalba, as it was jokingly called.

The Villalbas hoped a miracle awaited them in Allende. They traveled the balance of the day and through the night, stopping only to refuel from containers of gas they carried with them in the trucks. The vehicles were in good repair though it wasn't easy to keep them running. The only mechanic in the immediate area worked for the Chisos mining company. If a vehicle needed parts or repair, Federico had to travel to Marathon where he had purchased the vehicles. It was just as well. Federico hated to be beholden to Perry for anything. The Villalbas arrived in Allende at sunset of the following day. He immediately sent for the local *curandero*, or healer. He also sent for a priest. Both administered healing, one through herbs and chants, the other through prayer. Together, they offered hope.

The next few days were promising. María improved. Federico began to believe that the miracle he had prayed for was materializing. His joy, however, was short-lived. Unexpectedly, María's health deteriorated to where she could not take deep breaths without coughing heavily. Pneumonia was ravaging her body. The doctor who had taken the place of the *curandero* prescribed a narcotic to make her comfortable. She slept almost constantly. The doctor gave the Villalbas no more hope than had the doctor in the Big Bend. María lingered for a time. Finally, on November 26, 1918 María's premonition of death was realized.

The passing of his *querida* brought Federico to his knees like no man had ever been able to do. He felt every ounce of strength leave his body as his wife took her last breath. He could find no courage to replenish his bravado. There was only the fear of not knowing how he would continue without her. He married María when she was barely seventeen, and she gave him six children. Federico's dream was for the two of them to grow old together. His plans were for his boys to assume control of his businesses in the Big Bend, leaving him and his *reina*, his queen, to retire to his family's ranch in Aldama. His thoughts were muddled and futile.

What now? He asked himself. Federico was inconsolable in the coming days. Slowly, he began to emerge from his pain. He had an obligation to his family to regain his senses and direction. Federico began planning for the days to come. He had come to Allende to take his family out of harms way and had failed on one count; he wasn't about to fail on any others.

Days before, he had heard that the movie house in Allende was for sale. The thought of buying it had not registered until now. The family's return to the Big Bend would be ill advised, considering Jacobo's run-in with Det Walker. Word around town was that Walker had sworn to kill Jacobo, if he ever got the chance. Federico bought the movie house.

On February 26, 1919 Golla gave birth to a gorgeous baby girl they named María after her grandmother. The Villalbas tended to the theatre and a store Federico had purchased. As he had done in Study Butte, Jorge ran the store. Not one to sit idle, Federico managed the small ranch the family had acquired providing meat for the family's store as well as other stores in town.

It appeared as if Federico had no immediate plans to return to the Big Bend. He feared for his children's welfare in a land that seemed to resent their presence. His children, however, were more hopeful than fearful. Finally, after much debate, they convinced their father to return the family to the Big Bend. For all but Federico and Jacobo, arrangements were made to leave Allende in spring. Federico was not ready to return. He would remain behind to sell the ranch. He would hang on to the store and the theatre as he had plans for Jacobo to remain behind to manage the two until he felt it was safe for him to return home. Federico left for the Big Bend on December 26. Manuela, the young lady Jacobo had met, made his staying behind easier, but the thought of remaining too much longer past his father's departure never entered his mind. He was not afraid of Det Walker or any other man, for that matter.

The family returned to the Big Bend to find a depressed economy. World War I had ended November of the previous year. Had it not been for the dramatic drop in demand for quicksilver and the accompanying plummet in price, the end of the "Great War" might have gone unnoticed. The flu's devastation had decimated Terlingua and the outlying towns. Many of Federico's friends, Mexican and Anglo alike, had been lost to the illness.

Perry's mine had continued to operate, but at a greatly reduced output. Many of those who had survived the flu left the area to find work elsewhere. Some took jobs with the railroads; others returned to México. Those who stayed in the Big Bend attempted to settle back in to a pre-war lifestyle.

Remembering María

Upon selling the ranch, Federico returned to the Big Bend in April. He quickly busied himself with his ranch and businesses. He visited his Study Butte store and his cantina, *La Fiesta*, to survey their condition. He sat and talked to each of the employees that he had left in charge while Jorge inventoried the stock. The conversations were difficult. The store had been María's pride and joy. Like in their home, her personality was everywhere. Federico remembered when the store had opened. On her first visit to *La Tiendita*, María saw that her husband had insisted on placing ranch supplies and feed at the front of the store.

"What were you thinking?" he remembered her asking.

"I placed what was heaviest towards the front of the store," he answered innocently.

"*¡Hombres!*" she exclaimed with laughter.

"Who comes to the store most often?" she demanded. Before Federico could muster a word, she answered for him. "Women, of course. Household goods and supplies should be placed at the front of the store where it is most convenient for the women!"

He knew she was right. Instead of admitting it though, he recalled how he riled her a bit more.

"Feed and leather goods are so heavy, *mi corazón*," Federico said, feigning despair.

María shook her head and smiled at her husband's silliness. "Lazy men," she proclaimed.

"Help me," she ordered, as she picked up a heavy saddle and carried it to the back of the store.

Federico laughed as he grabbed the saddle from her.

"Sit," he remembered saying. "Jorge and I will do as you wish."

Federico wiped moisture from his eyes with his shirtsleeve as he continued his inventory. As it turned out, his mercantile businesses were in decent shape, but he was very low or entirely out of some goods. Though his credit with his suppliers was excellent, several had refused to continue deliveries during the family's absence, fearing that they might not return. Jorge would mend fences and take care of ordering stock. The following day, a Sunday, Federico and Santos rode out to his foreman's house to look over the ranch.

Emilio emerged from his *jacal*, or shack, as he heard hoof steps arrive at his door. He knew of Doña María's passing. His emotions were mixed. He was happy to see Don Federico, yet extremely sad to know that his *patrón* had returned without his wife.

"I am so sorry," he said, embracing Federico.

"*Gracias, mi amigo,*" Federico said. "I miss her very much."

Federico quickly masked his sadness with business. "What's happening with my ranch?"

"Since my last letter to you, we retrieved thirty head that had been rustled and sold to a rancher by the name of Gutiérrez in Santa Elena, but sadly we lost another twenty," Emilio said. "The brand had been altered, but it wasn't difficult to tell that it was ours."

"How many of them were longhorn?" Federico asked.

"All but three," Emilio said.

"Any of the Brahmas?"

"No."

"What do the *avisadores* say?"

"Anglos, as usual," Emilio said with little hesitation.

There was a short pause before Emilio continued. "Will Jacobo be going with me to retrieve our cattle?" Emilio asked.

"He stayed behind to take care of some family business. He'll return later," Federico said. He didn't feel it necessary to go into any details.

Holding the Family Together

On the morning of the next day, Santos was antsy. Once back at the ranch, he wanted to get to work. He knew his and Jacobo's good friend Valentín, the son of Candelario Baiza of Santa Elena, was somewhere on the ranch herding cattle. Valentín started working at Rancho Barras when he was twelve. Santos asked his father if he could join Valentín. The two were close in age and Federico knew that their getting together meant more shenanigans than work. But this was one time he didn't mind. Maybe it would take his son's mind off María's death.

The Baizas were *chiveros*, goat ranchers. Federico and his family were often criticized by his fellow Mexican cattle ranchers for maintaining a friendship with the Baizas. It was an unwritten rule that cattle ranchers were not to associate with *chiveros*, much less the Baizas, in particular. They had a reputation for being rabble-rousers. It seemed like one Baiza or another was always in trouble with the law. Federico scoffed at the elitists. There was discrimination enough coming at them from the Anglos. Why add to the ignorance?

Santos saw a horseman in the distance and yelled, "Valentín!" He knew it was his friend by the pinto he rode. Even at 14, Valentín took great pride in his horsemanship. The young man made sure that his horse and tack were always well cared for. The well polished silver ornaments on the saddle gleamed in the sun as Santos approached. Federico had given Valentín the saddle just before María became ill, as a reward for his hard work and for being a good friend to his sons.

"¡*Esquincle*, little snot-nose!" Valentín shouted back as he nudged his horse into a gallop towards his amigo.

They dismounted and hugged. The boys had known each other all their lives and couldn't be closer if they were kin. Word of Santos' mother's passing had spread fast once it arrived in Terlingua.

Valentín's eyes filled with tears. "I am so sorry, my brother."

"*Gracias*," Santos responded.

"How is your *papá*—your family?"

"My father cries at night. It is sad. We all miss her very much. Regina accompanied Uncle Max to Fort Davis."

"How are you doing, *manito*, little brother?" Valentín asked as he squeezed Santos' shoulders.

"I cry too…by myself." Santos said. This was something he would confide only to his friend.

Valentín changed the subject. "I heard Cobito didn't return." Cobito was a nickname that Jacobo allowed only his closest friends and family to call him.

Santos eyes gleamed with excitement. "Papá bought a theatre, a store and a small ranch at Allende. Can you believe it?" he said. "Papá sold the ranch before he returned. Jacobo stayed back to sell the store and the theatre."

"Good thing. That Walker is gunning for him," Valentín said with concern in his eyes.

"Jacobo can take care of himself," said Santos.

"*Manito*, I know he can, as long as he and Walker are face to face. Remember, Walker knows Cobito is faster than he is. Do you think he's going to fight fair?"

"It's best your brother stayed in México, at least for now," Valentín said.

"I guess you're right. Hey, let's go fishing," Santos said.

"Your father will get upset?"

"Don't worry about him. We'll go just for an hour or two."

Valentín slapped his reins, first against his chaps and then against the horse's backside. "*¡Vámonos!*"

The boys headed for the Rio Grande where they had fishing poles hidden along the riverbank for impromptu moments such as this. It was a good day. Two hours turned into the entire day. What catfish they didn't eat for lunch they took home for dinner.

Federico "Lico" Jr. mourned his mother's death quietly. Of all of the Villalba children, his manner was most like his father's. He was reserved and soft-spoken. Even so, one always knew where he stood on issues. Once he chose a battle, he was relentless. Though María would never admit to having a favorite child, she was partial to Lico. He had a calming effect on his siblings, especially on Regina and Jacobo, whose tempers flared at the drop of a hat.

At nineteen, Lico knew that with Felipe in El Paso and Jorge with the responsibility of his family and the store, the lion's share of helping regain the family's foothold fell squarely on his shoulders. There would be no help from Regina or Jacobo who were both away from home. Santitos was still a child.

Lico stood with his father looking at the expanse of the land before him. Its beauty did little to take his mind off of his mother.

"Papá, what are we going to do?"

"We go on with life, my son. We finish what we started," he said.

Federico's Chisos Land is Stolen

While struggling to regain his foothold, to add insult to injury, Federico learned from a fellow rancher that a nasty rumor was circulating that his Chisos property was no longer recognized as Villalba land. A trip to Alpine transformed the rumor into reality. Public records reflected that whoever converted ownership rights was expert enough to erase any record of Federico ever having had claim to the property. Federico immediately traveled to Marfa to hire the law firm of Mead & Metcalfe to assist him in reclaiming the land.

A Changing of the Guard

Howard Perry, in 1919, formed a partnership with Wayne Cartledge and founded La Harmonia Company. Shortly after, Wayne stepped down from his position as Chisos mine superintendent, handing over the reins to his younger brother Robert Cartledge. La Harmonia's initial venture was a trading post in Castolón. In 1923 they expanded their business to include cotton farming and in the late 1920's they added ranching to the company's activities. Cartledge, with his son Eugene, managed the business.

3

Bootlegging and a New Housekeeper

In Allende, a day didn't go by where Jacobo wasn't thinking about returning to his home. Running the movie house and handling the sale of the store had become tedious, as had the relationship with his girlfriend. Jacobo had been reading and hearing about the Volstead Act and the new Eighteenth Amendment passed in the United States installing prohibition. The buzz around town was how much the *Norte Americano's* silliness would mean to Northern Mexico's economy.

Over poker, several of his buddies started bragging about the money they made taking liquor to the border and selling it to bootleggers. They talked of wanting to take the liquid refreshment across the border and double, maybe even triple their profit, but admitted it was far too risky. They'd leave that to the *contrabandistas*.

The wheels started turning in Jacobo's mind. He knew the Río Grande like the back of his hand. There were places to cross that not even the most cunning *diablo* would know to look. He convinced himself that he could ferry liquor across without getting caught. There was one obstacle, however, even greater than the *diablos*. His father.

Federico had the reputation of being straight laced. Jacobo was reasonably certain that his father would balk at becoming involved in any illegal venture. This didn't stop him from researching the business enterprise. Jacobo started making inquiries and contacts. Unbeknownst to the family, he traveled to Santa Elena on several occasions, shouting distance from Rancho Barras. He went to inquire about the production of sotol, cousin to tequila. Sotol was the drink of choice in the Big Bend. More than eight centuries before, México's Tarahumara Indians discovered the wild *agavacea*, a plant similar to the blue agave, in the Northern region of México's Sierra Madre Mountains. The natives called the plant sotol, which means desert spoon. They cooked the plant's *piña*, heart, and fermented the elixir. The potent liquor was used for religious rituals and ceremonies. The Spanish took sotol to another level, distilling it and serving it to guests at their haciendas.

While in the border town, Jacobo discovered that sotol, beer, tequila and mescal were being stockpiled in larger quantities than could be moved by the *contrabandistas*. He returned to Allende more convinced than ever that this was something he could do. Now all he had to do between now and his return to Terlingua was put the final touches on a plan that would make the venture work. More important than that, was trying to figure a way of convincing his father to become a part of the undertaking.

Smuggling liquor from México marked the beginning of a new and very profitable, albeit, notorious chapter in the Big Bend's history. The money that could be made by way of this shady venture was far too alluring for some of the more prominent citizens of the Big Bend. Prohibition was too unpopular for strict enforcement in the Big Bend. Bootleggers had few problems with the local constabulary. Unless they broke more serious laws, there was no motivation to curtail their activities. Bootlegging also brought a left-handed peace to the area, since many Anglos wanted liquor and a business relationship with Mexicans. Bootlegging was the way to get it.

The Texas Rangers were not so accommodating. Intricate and sophisticated smuggling networks were established to keep the rangers off the scent. In some instances, the *sotoleros*, a word that became synonymous with bootleggers, took a more direct approach; it is rumored that some *diablos* were paid very handsomely to look the other way.

Smuggling sotol across the Rio Grande

Predictably, Jacobo's father chose to steer clear of any involvement with the *sotoleros*. Though many of his friends became involved as active participants or as financiers, there was just too much at stake for him. This is not to say that he didn't occasionally take a delivery of liquor—for medicinal purposes, of course.

Regina had returned from Marfa and had grown restless. She was not allowed to work on the ranch with the boys and only infrequently permitted to work at the store. Since her return, she had been relegated to housekeeper. Regina made it clear to her father that she did not want to become housekeeper and caretaker to her siblings.

One day Federico had just returned from his morning coffee when Regina approached him. She appeared upset about something. Federico braced himself.

"Papá, I resent the fact that you consider me nothing more than a maid," she said. "I don't mind doing for you, but Santos and Lico can take care of themselves. Why do you need me to help look after them?"

"*Mi hija*, I have no desire to argue with you. With your mother gone, I am lost. She was a strong woman and did so much. Until I get my bearings, I need your help. I promise you that soon we will hire someone to help with the womanly chores."

"That's fine," she said. "Will you let me help on the ranch?"

"You can help Jorge with the store," Federico said.

"If it's the *diablos* you're worried about, I can take care of myself," Regina said.

"I know you can, but I already have sufficient *vaqueros*. Where I need you is here, supervising the cooks and the housekeeper I will hire. As time permits, you can spend more time at the stores. Just stay away from the caramels," Federico said with a big smile.

As a little girl, anytime Regina went to the store the caramels kept in a coffee tin at the counter would mysteriously disappear. No one ever figured how she smuggled them out of the store unseen. In Federico's eyes, Regina was still his little girl. He could never live with himself if she came to be harmed.

In deference to his daughter's wishes, Federico immediately began interviewing for a housekeeper. His neighbor, Dolores García, told him that he would talk to his sister, Severa, to see if she might be interested.

Dolores García (left) and Federico Villalba

Severa García lived with her brother and knew the Villalbas well. Before María died, she would come to the ranch and pray the *novenas* (nine days of prayers to obtain special graces) with Doña

María and to teach the children catechism. She gladly accepted the responsibility. "Severita" as the family called her, was a tiny but striking and willful woman. It would take time and some head butting with Regina, but she would find a place in the family's routine and later, in their hearts.

Severa "Severita" García

Jacobo's Temptation

In August 1921, Jacobo returned to Terlingua with his father. Federico had traveled to Allende to finalize the sale of the theatre and accompany his son back to the Big Bend. He was proud of his son. Jacobo had done a fine job of managing the family interests. They turned a nice profit. The two of them set out on their trip back to their home in good spirits.

"*Jefecito*, how are things at home?" Jacobo asked as they drove through the countryside.

"Severita García has come to the house to help us," his father said.

Jacobo looked at his father and smiled, "I know, Regina wrote and told me."

"She's a good person," Federico said.

"How is *la princesa* getting along with her?"

"You know your sister. It was difficult in the beginning, but they eventually saw eye-to-eye. They're getting along well now."

"And Jorge, how is he doing?"

"He's doing fine. He has his hands full with his family and running the store. I rarely see him on the ranch anymore."

Jacobo smiled broadly at his father. "I can't wait to see Lico and Santos."

"I assure you, they can't wait to see you either. They've got a lot of work waiting for you," Federico said, smiling devilishly.

"Have we lost more cattle?"

"None, since I returned. I'm having two men stay with the herd each night. The uninvited won't live to see daylight," Federico said.

"Any trouble with the law?"

Federico took a deep breath and glanced over his shoulder at his son.

"With the sheriff, no problems, with the Rangers, always," he said.

"It's a shame our people have to walk around in fear. As for me, what happens, happens," Jacobo said.

Federico shook his head at his son's arrogance. It was good he had him stay in México, he thought. They rode in silence for the next few miles. Federico was trying to rest; Jacobo was working up the courage to talk to him about bootlegging.

"Papá, there is something I want to talk to you about," he said, his heart pounding. "There is much money being made by bringing liquor into Texas. Have you considered becoming involved?"

Federico knew his son well enough to recognize that he would not be asking this question unless he'd already given it much thought.

"No," Federico responded, shaking his head. "It's far too risky. Besides, we don't need to be involved in anything illegal while we're fighting to get back our Chisos property."

"If it's done properly, there is no risk Papá," Jacobo said.

Federico became irritated at Jacobo's impertinence.

"Enough! I said no!" Federico said. "We are not becoming *contrabandistas* and that's it. I've tired of this conversation."

"Don't get angry, Papá—you're right. The money is not worth the risk," Jacobo agreed but only to pacify his father.

Jacobo had been bootlegging liquor for over six months. Grease the right palms, and there was no danger. He wasn't about to tell his father that, at least not yet.

Federico and Jacobo arrived at the ranch to find the house full of people. Federico had wired ahead to let the family know when they would arrive. Lico, Regina, Santos, Jorge and Golla, pregnant with a third child, greeted them. Severita was in the kitchen putting the final touches on dinner.

"Welcome home, little brother," Lico said as he hugged Jacobo.

"How did it go?" Regina asked, stepping in to take her turn at welcoming her brother.

"It went well," he answered.

"What about Manuela?" Regina asked. "We thought for sure you'd bring her home."

"She was a diversion—nothing more," Jacobo said, smiling.

"*Como eres canalla*, you are such a cad," Regina said.

"Ready to go fishing?" Santos interrupted with a big smile. He could care less about some silly girl.

"Ready," Jacobo said, reaching around Santos neck and pulling his little brother to him. "I bet you and Valentín have done your share of fishing in my absence."

"More of that than work," Lico chimed in.

"Let's eat," Federico decreed. "We can talk over dinner."

Jacobo smiled and gently poked at María's tummy as he picked her up.

"And who is this little doll?" he said, walking with her to the dinner table. Named after their mother, the sight of the little angel brought Jacobo happiness and understandably, a tinge of sadness.

Severita entered just as the family sat at the table. She greeted Federico with a coy smile as she placed a basket of biscuits in front of him. Federico returned the smile. Federico was not prone to smiling. Amused at the exchange between the two, Jacobo quickly looked around the table to see if anyone else had caught it. If they had, no one seemed to react. He shook his head, inwardly embarrassed that his imagination might have gotten the best of him.

"Severita, how are you?" he asked as he reached for the *frijoles*.

"*Bien, gracias a Dios*," she said.

"Have you been taking good care of my father?" Jacobo teased.

"She's taken good care of all of us," Federico answered before Severita could muster a response.

The sight and smell of biscuits brought back memories. Federico had never cared for tortillas. María always had a basket of biscuits baked by the time Federico strolled into the kitchen for his morning coffee. Severita had graciously accepted and carried on the tradition.

4

The School Teacher

Born in 1895 in Candela, Coahuila, México, Miguel had first come to the Big Bend via Ojinaga, Chihuahua, at the age of nineteen. As a young lieutenant in Pancho Villa's revolutionary army, Miguel rode into Ojinaga to battle *federales* on January 10, 1914. Miguel was injured when his horse was shot out from under him. The horse fell against an outcropping of rocks, crushing his right leg.

Painfully inching his way out from under the dead horse, Miguel crawled to safety. It was nearly nine o'clock in the evening. The *federales* and their sympathizers fled in all directions. The sun had long disappeared. January had been the coldest month of the winter. Unable to tell whether he was losing feeling in his leg because of the loss of blood or the bitter cold, Miguel lay against the rocks with his ammunition and energy spent. Lapsing in and out of consciousness, he suddenly felt a firm nudge on his shoulder. He opened his eyes expecting to see the enemy and the barrel of a gun pointed at his head. Instead, he saw a civilian who identified himself as a *villista*. Miguel was taken to a small village near the battleground where a local doctor treated him.

Miguel stayed with his rescuer, Eziquiel Palacios, for the six months it took him to recuperate. Well enough to ride but with a noticeable limp, which he would have the rest of his life, he returned to his home in Villa Unión.

Pancho Villa flanked by Emiliano Zapata to his left and surrounded by some of his trusted troops

There, he resumed his teaching career at the *secundaria,* or high school level. Generally speaking, Miguel was a man of propriety. He was respected in the community, known well for his oratorical skills. Had he chosen to stay, he would have had a good life in Villa Unión. He was, however, drawn to a land he had seen only through the jaded eyes of war but remembered as a land of beauty and opportunity.

In late 1919, he decided to return to Northern Chihuahua. One year later, he crossed the river to Texas with the hope of teaching. He had heard that Mexican children were allowed to attend Anglo schools, but were required to speak English. Many didn't. Children complained that they weren't learning anything so, right or wrong, some parents kept their children home. There were no schools that taught in Spanish.

He decided that it might be of value to approach Mexican ranchers who had young children. Perhaps they would hire him as a tutor. It was an idea that was well received. He found work and he traveled to various ranches, spending two or three days at each place. He charged 25 cents per day per child. Some families were able to pay, some not. He would make ends meet by accepting room and board and by taking photos for a dime apiece with his Brownie camera. It was while traveling from one ranch to another that he first met Federico Villalba.

It was a warm morning. The mule was slowly pulling his buckboard, and, it seemed to Miguel, enjoying the scenery as much as he was. Neither was in a hurry. Some distance ahead, a plume of dust became longer and closer. Miguel reached into the satchel beneath his feet and pulled out his Colt .45, placing it on the seat beside him. He could see that it was a lone horseman and too well dressed to be a bandit.

The man slowed from a hard gallop to a trot and finally to a walk. He pulled his horse up next to the buckboard. Sitting astride a large, heaving chestnut that must have been a full eighteen hands, was an imposing barrel-chested gentleman with piercing blue eyes. After a brief acknowledging glance towards Miguel, followed by a quick survey of the gun and the back of the buckboard full of books and supplies, the man spoke.

"Are you the *maestro* they speak of in town?" he asked.

Miguel sat straight and proud as he answered.

"I am indeed. Miguel Esquivel González to serve you," he said. According to Mexican custom, a child is given the first surname from the father. The second surname is the mother's maiden name.

"My name is Federico Villalba Jasso. I am in need of a *tintero*. Are you for hire?" he asked.

"I am a teacher, not a bookkeeper," Miguel said.

"Can you keep books?"

"I can," Miguel answered, annoyed at the man's brashness. "I have no interest in doing so."

"I can offer you full-time work at $20 per month, plus room and board," Federico declared, undaunted by Miguel's inflexibility.

This was nearly twice what Miguel had been able to make as a roving teacher. Even so, he could not betray his principles.

"I must decline your offer. As I said before, I am a teacher, not a bookkeeper."

"Ask anyone how to get to the Rancho Barras. I will see you in one week."

Federico dug his boots into the chestnut's flanks and galloped off without waiting for any affirmation from the bespectacled teacher.

The man's arrogance was intolerable, Miguel thought. Even if he were of a mind to take the job, he wasn't all that certain that he could work for someone of that temperament. The buckboard lurched forward with a flick of the reins. *How dare the man presume that he would give up his job as a teacher.* Even so, he would ask around about this Villalba fellow.

Rustlers

Two days after his encounter with Miguel, one of Federico's *vaqueros* was grazed by a poacher's bullet. Federico arranged for a meeting with Brewster County Sheriff Everett Townsend. He intended to discuss his ongoing battle with rustlers.

Federico's overriding motive was to set the record straight with Townsend. Ordinarily, he and his boys would have taken care of this business. If the rustlers happened to be Mexican, their demise wouldn't be challenged. In fact, it might even be celebrated. These men, however, were *gringos*. This could cause complications, something Federico didn't need.

Born in 1871, Everett Ewing Townsend joined the Texas Rangers at age nineteen. He was appointed a deputy United States marshal three years later and in 1894, chosen to be a United States customs mounted inspector and given charge of improving some 200,000 acres of free range in Pecos County. Elected Sheriff in 1918, he had been top lawman now for five years. He'd known Federico since his Ranger days and had become good friends with the man.

"I heard what happened the other night," Townsend said. "I'm glad you came to me, Fred. I need you and your boys to keep your guns holstered until I can find out who's doing the rustling."

"I know who they are," Federico declared.

"Now Fred, you don't know that for sure?" Townsend said.

Federico looked at Everett with certainty in his eyes. "I'm sure."

Townsend didn't argue with his friend. Federico had drawn his own conclusions from whatever information he retrieved from the "Mexican grapevine." There was no way he would convince Federico otherwise.

"You just be sure and tell that son of yours, Jake, to keep his gun holstered. He's a hothead. I don't want him taking the law into his own hands," Townsend said.

"You take care of the rustlers. I'll take care of my son," Federico said.

Townsend was right. Jacobo was a match that lit with very little pressure.

Jacobo sat impatiently at Chata Sada's home café in Boquillas, not far from the Texas Ranger office where Sheriff Townsend had arranged to meet Federico. He had accompanied his father to Boquillas but had not been allowed to take part in the meeting. He scooped the last bit of *frijoles* with a piece of corn tortilla he used like a spoon and was about to put it in his mouth when his father walked into the café.

"What did *el cherife* say?" Jacobo asked. At the moment, Federico thought it more important to order a cup of coffee than to answer his son's question.

Jacobo repeated his question, this time in a measured tone. "Papá, what did Townsend say?"

Federico mimicked drinking a cup of coffee as Chata finally looked over from where she was delivering food to a customer. She nodded and smiled. Federico looked over at his son. "He told me to keep your nose out of his business."

Jacobo saw no amusement in his father's comment or his disinterested demeanor.

"Is he going after the rustlers?"

"He's going to look into it."

"That worthless!" Jacobo exclaimed, throwing his tortilla and beans back onto his plate.

"Settle down. Let the man do his job. This is a big Texas, my son," said Federico, pausing in reflection. "We will deal with many challenges. Our responsibility is to maintain our civility and not be drawn into violence by scoundrels. No man should have the power to draw us away from our dreams. Anglos may see us as an inferior people, incapable of ruling our lives and shaping our own destiny, but history will see us different. This land prospers because of our wisdom, our blood and our sweat. This will be our legacy. The rustlers will have to answer to the law.

Jacobo wasn't as restrained or as philosophical as his father. In his mind, treachery's just reward was the business ends of his six-shooters, two pearl handled .45 caliber Colts.

Miguel arrives at Rancho Barras

Out the corner of her eye, Regina noticed an unfamiliar mule and buckboard approaching from the east. Standing under the *ramada*, she squinted into the sun trying to distinguish the features of the man at the reins. Earlier in the week at the dinner table, her father had spoken of a conversation he'd had with a man about the bookkeeping position. This appeared to be the man and the rig her father had described.

It was early morning. She and Severita had just finished supervising the feeding of the *vaqueros* when the buckboard reached the shelter.

Miguel stepped down from the wagon slapping dust off of his clothes. He noticed two ladies looking at him intently, one of them gripping the handle of a gun strapped to her waist.

"Good day. My name is Miguel Esquivel González. I am here to see Don Federico Villalba about the bookkeeping job."

Regina studied the man before she spoke.

"I am his daughter, Regina. My father is in Boquillas on business this morning. He should return later this afternoon."

Miguel marveled at Regina's beauty. The strong tanned features of her face framed by her coal black hair were mesmerizing.

Regina Villalba (age 17) in Study Butte

"May I wait for him?" Miguel asked, struggling to maintain his concentration.

"If you want," Regina answered with an indifferent shrug of her shoulders.

Miguel looked at Regina's eyes and smiled.

"May I trouble you for some coffee?"

"My, you are a pushy one aren't you," she teased.

Severita grinned at her stepdaughter's playfulness. It was apparent that Miguel's good looks had made an impression on Regina.

Pleased that Regina smiled back at him, Miguel responded politely.

"It was a long ride. I just need something to wash the dust out of my mouth; perhaps a drink of water."

"Sit down," Regina commanded. "I will get you both. Are you hungry? I will have the cook prepare you breakfast."

"Thank you, but no. Coffee will be sufficient."

Jorge, who had come from Study Butte to speak with his father, noticed the buckboard and a stranger talking to his sister under the *ramada*. He spurred his horse into a full gallop. Ten feet from the *ramada* Jorge pulled back hard on the reins and dismounted as his horse slid to a stop on his haunches, raising a cloud of dust. The momentum carried him quickly to the table where the man sat.

"Who are you?" Jorge demanded to know, looking at Miguel.

"My name is Miguel Esquivel González. Who are you?"

"Jorge Villalba," he answered, amused by the bravado in the little man's voice. "State your business."

"Don Federico, who I assume is your father, wished to hire me as his bookkeeper."

"Give me a coffee," Jorge ordered the cook. He grabbed a chair from the table, turned it backwards and straddled it. Jorge pulled a kerchief out of his back pocket, took off his hat and wiped the sweat and dust off his brow as he continued speaking. He looked up to Regina who stood silently by the table.

"Don't you have something to do?" he asked.

His sister glared at him. She said nothing, but only because of the stranger's presence. Her brother would never have gotten away with talking to her in that manner had they been alone. She left for the house in a huff.

"*Papá* tells me you are a teacher," Jorge said, unfazed by his sister's performance.

"I am."

"Where are you from?

"Villa Unión, Coahuila."

"What brings you to Terlingua?"

"I came to Ojinaga back in '14 with Villa. I returned last year and decided to come across the border to teach. I heard there were no schools for the Mexican youngsters."

"You rode with Villa...you were in the war?" Jorge was intrigued by Miguel's claim.

"Yes, I was injured. That's why I walk with a cane," he said, pointing to the walking stick leaning against the table.

"You were shot?"

"No, my horse was. He fell on me. His name was Tordillo. He was a good horse."

Jorge was tempted to laugh, but didn't. Riding with Villa was impressive and deserved respect.

"Can you still ride a horse?" Jorge queried.

"Of course I can, and I can still shoot a gun," Miguel said, sipping his coffee and looking at Jorge over the rim of his glasses in mild amusement.

"So are you going to take the job? Papá said you weren't too excited about the offer when you two spoke."

"Actually, he did most of the speaking, but, yes, I will take the job if it's still available. I could use the money. I was hoping your father would allow me to teach on my days off."

Jorge laughed. "You expect days off?"

Miguel's expectation gave way to apprehension. He hoped Jorge was joking.

Regina, in the meantime, was still fuming about the way Jorge had treated her. She was rehearsing what she would say to her brother when the opportunity presented itself. Being the only girl had presented its tribulations over the years, not the least was continuously having to prove her equality. She was as good, or better, at whatever her brothers could do except for one drawback, her femininity. Her mother had taught her to be a lady. It was something her brothers appreciated, but at the same time regarded as a weakness.

The Teacher Becomes a Bookkeeper

Federico and Jacobo returned to the ranch in the afternoon. They spotted the buckboard, mule and then the gentleman slumped over dozing on the bench in front of the house. Federico smiled as he spurred his horse into a slow gallop.

"*El Maestro*," Federico declared.

"Who is he going to teach?" Jacobo asked. Santos, the youngest, was already fourteen. Their mother had taught them all to read and write. What they didn't learn from her, they learned from necessity.

"I offered him a job as a bookkeeper."

Miguel woke at the sound of the horses' neigh as the Villalbas approached the *ramada*. He stood up and rubbed the sleep out his eyes as Federico dismounted and approached.

"So you decided to come," Federico said.

"I did, but first we must discuss my wage," Miguel said.

"We decided on $20 per month."

"That was your decision, Don Federico, not mine. I will work for you, but for nothing less than $40 per month, and I must have two days to teach."

"That's more than my *vaqueros* earn. Why should I pay you that much?"

"*Señor*, you are not forced to pay me anything, no more than I am forced to work for you. My work is my reputation. I believe my

Miguel Esquivel González - "Maestro"

education and reputation are worth $40 per month. If you do not agree, I will leave, and you may continue your search for a book-keeper. I am certain that there are candidates out there who feel that their worth is less." Miguel grabbed his cane, and with a tip of the hat began walking to the buckboard.

Federico looked at Jacobo, shook his head in amusement and smiled.

"Forty dollars a month. For that much money, you must also help my sons on the ranch whenever there is a need."

"May I teach on my day off?" Miguel asked.

Federico laughed, "If you have the strength."

Federico introduced him to his other sons pointing at each in quick succession.

"This is the youngest, Santos, we call him *esquincle*; the ugly one next to Santos is Lico. He's a newlywed. Lico had recently married María, the 18-year-old daughter of Rosendo Avila, one of the *vaqueros*. Over there is my second youngest, Jacobo. You've met my daughter and *Chochi*, Jorge's nickname."

"I have indeed," Miguel responded. "Now if someone will show me to my quarters, and where I will tend to your books, I will start today if you wish."

"Tomorrow's soon enough," Federico said. "Jacobo will show you to your quarters."

Miguel spent the balance of the day reading. It was his passion.

5

The Bookkeeper Becomes a Bronco Buster

Jacobo's booming voice stirred Miguel violently from his morning slumber.

"Time to get up, *Maestro*."

It was the break of dawn. *No bookkeeping today*, Miguel thought. After his morning devotional, he proceeded to the *ramada* where Jacobo greeted him.

"Today you work with us."

"*Lo sé.* What will we be doing?" Miguel asked.

"Whatever needs to be done. Come sit with us."

Miguel followed Jacobo to the table where the other Villalbas sat.

Miguel nodded to the group.

"Where is your sister?" Miguel asked.

"She's in the house," Jorge responded. "Don't get any ideas *maestro*. She's engaged."

Miguel said nothing. He sat and poured himself some coffee while the others chuckled at Jorge's commentary.

"Don't worry, *Maestro*, you'll see her later. Right now, eat. We have much to do today. You will need your strength."

The men finished breakfast and went directly to the barn to saddle up and prepare to ride out to the range. For Miguel, Lico had cut out a little white-faced *mesteño*, a mustang stallion that stood about thirteen hands. Descendants of the horses brought over from Spain, the herd of mustangs the Villalba's found on their land were most likely left behind by the Comanche.

"Does it have a name?" Miguel asked, cinching the saddle Jacobo had handed him.

"The one you give him," Jacobo said.

Miguel thought for a moment and then spoke.

"I will name him Lucky," he announced, glancing over at the Villalba brothers with a telling smirk.

"You're pretty sure of yourself," Lico said to the schoolteacher.

"Is that a question or an observation?" Miguel asked.

"I suppose, a little of both," Lico said.

Santos handed jerky, two canteens full of water and a supply of biscuits to his brothers and some to the "cocky one." After stowing the food in his saddlebag and tying the leather straps of his canteens to the saddle horn, Jacobo went to the last stall in the barn to saddle his father's horse.

"Don Federico is accompanying us?" Miguel asked.

"He wants to see you in action," Jacobo kidded. "Why didn't you tell him you rode with Villa?"

"I didn't see any point in it."

"Perhaps its good thing you didn't tell him. He doesn't care for Villa. He calls him the 'accidental hero'."

"It would appear that a debate is on the horizon," Miguel said.

"Not if you want to continue your employment," Jacobo shot back.

Just then Federico strolled into the barn.

"Lazy ones, what is taking so long? It gets hotter as each minute goes by. *Maestro*, are you at fault?" Federico asked.

Miguel was embarrassed at having been singled out.

"I am ready," Miguel declared purposefully as he buckled his chaps and quickly mounted his horse.

Jacobo delivered the chestnut to his father, holding on to the reins as Federico stuck his boot in the stirrup and stepped up into the saddle, spurs a-jangling as he did. Santos and Lico were already outside the barn. Their horses danced with restlessness. As soon as Jacobo was settled into his saddle, Federico yelled *"Vámonos."*

"Maestro," Federico shouted over his shoulder. "Come up here with us."

Lico, being the oldest of the Villalba brothers present, rode in his rightful place at the front beside his father. Miguel trotted up to join them.

"Today, I am the teacher," Federico said. "I am going to teach you about survival in this beautiful but perilous land." Federico paused and looked over at Miguel.

"Tell me, when you rode for Villa, what did he promise you in return for your participation?"

Miguel remembered what Jacobo had said about Federico's disdain for Villa. *How had he found out?* he thought. He quickly came to the conclusion that Lico told his father as they rode alone up front, just out of earshot. What could he say that would not incite an argument?

"The man himself promised me nothing, Don Federico. The revolution, on the other hand, offered freedom from the oppression of Díaz. Villa represented a means of gaining that freedom."

"You have your freedom now. Why didn't you remain in México to enjoy it?" Federico asked.

"Freedom was imperative for my country, my people. For me individually, I remain a prisoner to my dreams which were never confined to Mexican borders."

Federico would ask Miguel nothing more about Villa. "School teacher, I make no promises except for one. I will demand of you no more or no less than I demand of myself. I hired you because you are a smart man. If you look after my best interests, I will look after yours. Are we in agreement?" Federico asked.

"We are," Miguel repeated, affirming their accord.

Federico's silence was Miguel's cue to rejoin Santos and Jacobo who trailed behind. "What are we going to do today," Miguel asked Jacobo.

Santos beat his brother to the answer. "We're going to break some horses," he said. Santos leaned forward in his saddle, so Miguel could see his devilish smile.

"I haven't broken a horse since before my injury," Miguel commented. "I don't know if I still can."

"We'll find out, won't we?" Jacobo said.

"I suppose we will," said Miguel.

Emilio, mi amigo," Federico shouted as they approached the corral. In the corral were ten infuriated *mesteños*, stomping and snorting, looking for a way to escape.

Lucky's neck jerked back then forward at the sight, causing Miguel to hold a tighter rein. It was obvious his horse remembered the freedom he once enjoyed. He was ready to bolt if his rider was careless.

"We will only break five," Federico announced.

"Which five?" Emilio asked.

"I'll take the paint. You four pick your own," Federico instructed his *compañeros*. Each picked a horse. The remainder were cut out and returned to the adjoining holding corral.

"I will go first," Miguel volunteered. He was anxious to get it over with. He dismounted and began to unsaddle his horse.

"Use this one," Emilio shouted, walking over to Miguel and handing him a saddle used especially for broncos.

Jacobo did his best to blind the horse with a hood, while Miguel struggled to saddle the bronc. The mustang bucked and heaved like a trod on rattler each time he felt leather touch his back. Jacobo slipped the rope halter over the horse's flaring nostrils, handing the tail ends to Miguel as he climbed onto eleven hundred pounds of fury. The animal broke away, bucking in short punctuated lurches. When he couldn't throw the rider, he changed his tactics to longer, more teeth-chattering leaps covering the width and length of the corral. Miguel felt the strength in his injured leg starting to give out. The horse seemed to be tiring, but not fast enough to suit the schoolteacher. Hard as he tried, he began to lose the battle. The next thing he felt was weightlessness then shortly thereafter an excruciating pain as his back met the desert floor.

Jacobo jumped into the corral and hastily dragged Miguel out before the horse could retaliate against his antagonist. "Are you all right, *maestro?*"

It took a moment for Miguel to regain his senses and his breath. "I don't think so," he said, groaning.

"Can you get up?" Jacobo asked.

"I may have broken my shoulder," Miguel said, as he rolled to his left, struggling to get up on his good side with Jacobo's assistance.

Federico was taking all of this in from the far side of the corral. "Finish the horse off!" he yelled to Emilio.

His foreman looked at his *patrón* in disappointment. He thought he'd be a mere spectator today. Luckily, the horse had very little fight left in him.

Federico saw Miguel's face grimace in pain. He instructed Emilio to have his *vaqueros* break the remaining horses. Jacobo helped Miguel onto his horse and the four headed back to the ranch.

"You gave the horse a battle," Federico said.

"I make no excuses. I tried to break his spirit, and I was soundly rewarded for the effort."

"There is no dishonor in losing to a worthy opponent," Federico said.

"No, just humiliation."

The men arrived at the ranch house to find that the ladies had not yet returned. It had been hoped they would attend to Miguel's injury.

"Let us take you to the doctor," Federico suggested.

Miguel had an aversion to doctors, less one. He opted to go to seek out the doctor who treated him for his leg injury.

"Let me rest today, Don Federico. With your permission, I will take myself to the doctor in Presidio who will give me herbs I can rub on my shoulder."

"*Maestro*, judging from the bump on your back, you're going to need more than just herbs," Jacobo said.

"The doctor will know best," Miguel said.

Regina and Severita had prearranged to travel to Study Butte as soon as the men departed for the range. Golla had gotten word to them that some new fabrics and lace had arrived from El Paso. Regina was especially excited. She would finally see the Catalonian lace she had ordered from Spain many months ago. They took the truck. Federico had instructed them to pick up supplies for the ranch, as well as items needed to restock *La Tiendita*.

"What do you think of the teacher? Do you think he's handsome?" Severita asked.

Regina glanced curiously across her shoulder at Severita. "Where did that come from?"

"I see the way you look at him. He seems to have caught your fancy—no?"

"No!" Regina exclaimed. "*Es una pulga*, he's a flea. Why would I have an interest in that little man? Besides, I'm engaged, remember."

"When was the last time you saw Francisco?" Severita asked.

"That's neither here nor there!"

"You haven't seen or heard from your fiancé in almost nine months. How do you know he doesn't have another girlfriend?" Severita asked.

"Enough! Miguel is nothing more than one of my father's employees."

Severita took a lighthearted swipe at Regina. "Oh, so now we're calling him by his first name, are we?" Severita said

"You're too much," Regina said, shaking her head in amusement. "Now let me drive without distraction otherwise we will wind up as part of the landscape."

It was dusk when the women returned. The truck bed was filled with supplies. Severita's lap was piled high with fabric.

"We were getting worried," Federico said as he walked down the porch steps.

"We had dinner with Jorge and Golla," Regina said.

"What do you have here?" Federico asked as he surveyed the colorful materials that all but cloaked Severita from view.

"Many dresses in the making and a few *mantillas,*" she said, smiling.

Lico, Jacobo and Santos walked across over from the bunkhouse.

"Hola Regina, Severita. How did it go?" Lico asked.

"It went well," Regina answered.

Before she could say more, Lico looked in his father's direction and spoke.

"Papá, the teacher is in a great deal of pain."

"Give him some sotol; it will take the edge off of the pain."

"*¿Qué pasó?*" Regina inquired of her father.

"He was thrown by a horse he was trying to break. He hurt his shoulder."

"Did you take him to a doctor?"

"He's taking himself tomorrow. Tell me, why are you so worried about the school teacher?" Federico asked with a look of mild bewilderment. "One of my men was shot last week. You didn't seem to be nearly as concerned about him."

"Miguel seems to be such a nice man," Severita responded, drawing Federico's attention away from Regina. "We're just sorry to hear that he was injured."

6

Courting Regina

The outhouse door bounced shut behind Santos as he spied Miguel's buckboard entering the compound. The schoolteacher had returned with his shoulder wrapped and his arm in a sling. Miguel returned from Presidio with an ample supply of foul-smelling salve that the doctor told him to massage into his shoulder blade at least once a day. Santos followed Miguel into the bunkhouse where his brothers were playing cards with some of the *vaqueros*. Jacobo and Lico greeted Miguel.

"What is that smelly concoction you brought back in that jar?" Jacobo asked.

"It's a salve I have to apply to my shoulder. I can't reach; perhaps the three of you can take turns helping me apply the *medicina*," Miguel said to the brothers.

Jacobo laughed. "In your dreams," he said.

"Don't look at me school teacher," Lico said.

Santos doubled over pretending to have the dry heaves.

"The smell makes me nauseous," Jacobo said, "Ask Regina to rub it on you."

Miguel looked from one brother to the other and shook his head. "Maybe I will," he said.

"Don't listen to Jacobo," Lico said. "Regina will shove it down your throat before you get her to rub it on your back."

Jacobo and Santos broke out laughing.

Miguel looked dejected. "Maybe I can get one of the *vaqueros* to help me," he said as the boys continued to laugh.

"Good luck," Jacobo said, laughing even louder.

Lico stopped laughing when he saw the pain and anguish in Miguel's face. "Join us for lunch, *maestro*." He thought a good meal and some congenial conversation might take his mind off of his troubles.

Regina came out to the *ramada* with her hands full of freshly made tortillas. She was surprised to see Miguel sitting at the table talking to her father. Miguel, who caught movement out to the corner of his eye, instinctively swung his head around to see who might be approaching the table. For a quick instant, he and Regina locked eyes. She immediately looked away, embarrassed, pretending not to have noticed him.

"Regina," Federico called to her.

How mischievous my father is, she thought. Now she would be forced to look in Miguel's direction and acknowledge his presence.

"*Sí, señor,*" she answered, trying hard to avoid any eye contact with Miguel.

"You were so worried about the school teacher, aren't you going to at least ask him how he's doing?"

"I can see he's still alive," Regina answered, refusing to address Miguel directly.

Miguel shook his head in ambivalence. Regina seemed like a nice enough lady, but there was an edge to her that he hoped was more contrived than genuine. He wondered if a stranger could ever succeed in breaking through the facade.

The Ice Queen Begins to Melt

The Villalbas and *vaqueros* left the *ramada*. Miguel took one last sip of his coffee and prepared to leave for the ranch office when Regina slipped over and sat next to him.

"How is your shoulder?" she asked.

"It hurts. I have this medicine the doctor gave me that I've not been able to apply that would make it feel better," Miguel said, and then paused. "Your brothers and the *vaqueros* refuse to help me."

"Go retrieve it and come back to the kitchen. I'll have Severita give you a hand."

"Thank you," Miguel said.

"For what?" Regina asked.

"For taking a moment to talk to me. Your kindness is appreciated."

"Do not go mistaking my kindness for weakness Miguel," Regina said, as she winked and walked toward the adobe.

Her calling him by his first name did not go unnoticed. Perhaps he'd found a chink in her armor.

Playing Nurse

As instructed, Miguel returned. "Señorita Villalba, I am here," he shouted through the open kitchen door.

Regina looked over to the door and blew at the wisp of hair dangling in front of her face. "Give me a moment," she said, scurrying to a cabinet on the other side of the kitchen.

Miguel sat and waited. Regina reappeared with hair in place, without her apron, with a towel draped across her right shoulder.

"Take off your shirt," she ordered.

"I thought Severita was going to help me," Miguel said, surprised and embarrassed at Regina's command.

"She's too busy. Now take off your shirt," she repeated.

Miguel began slowly unbuttoning his shirt.

"Hurry! Don't worry, with five brothers you think I'm going to be embarrassed at seeing a bare chest?" she laughed.

The Villalba men all had hairy chests. Miguel did not.

"It's not your embarrassment I'm concerned about," Miguel confessed. Miguel handed Regina the jar of salve.

"*Jesús, María y José,* this smells horrible," Regina said as she opened the jar. "What is it? It smells worse than the *mataguzanos,* maggot killer, we put on cattle sores."

"Señorita, if you find the odor too offensive, I'll try to find a way of putting it on myself," Miguel said, as he started to stand up.

"No, sit," Regina demanded as she pushed down on his shoulders. "I'll apply it, but only this once. I'm getting one of the helpers to apply it from here on in."

"Why did you come to work for my father?" Regina asked as she massaged the smelly goop into Miguel's shoulder blade.

"My father and brother wrote to tell me of a ranch they wanted to buy for the family near Ciudad Acuña. They asked if I would help to finance the purchase. I sent them what little I had saved and promised to send more. The only way I could do that was to make more money than I was making as a teacher."

"Am I hurting you?" Regina asked, as Miguel squirmed beneath her hands.

Miguel expelled the breath he was holding before answering. "A bit, but that's fine. I expected it would hurt to the touch."

"Do you have a wife?"

"Oh, goodness no!" Miguel exclaimed.

Regina smiled at Miguel's quick and animated response.

"Why, do you have something against marriage?"

"No, I've just never found the lady I wanted to marry," Miguel said, in plain words. "I understand you are engaged."

"Since I was eighteen. It seems like forever," she said.

"And why haven't you married?"

"He lives in Ciudad Chihuahua. We hardly see each other. Francisco's the son of my father's cousin. If I married him, I would have to live in México, something I do not want to do," she said.

"What's wrong with México?"

"*Miguelito*, you ask too many questions!" she said, punctuating her remark with a firm squeeze of his shoulder.

Miguel winced in pain blurting, "*¡Ay Dios mío!*"

"We're done," said Regina, cleaning her hands with a towel.

Not a moment too soon, Miguel thought. "*Gracias Señorita.*"

"You're welcome, and you may call me Regina," she said with what appeared to be a hint of a smile. Regina walked back to the kitchen door without further comment.

Miguel was becoming accustomed to the resilience in Regina's personality. Growing up with six men in the family had to have been difficult, most likely accounting for her hard crust. She was intriguing, to say the least.

Punching Cattle

The men were busy gathering their gear and three days worth of supplies for the cattle drive while Miguel was attended to. Once the wrangler had the small *remuda* of spare horses in tow, they said their goodbyes and departed to round up another 50 head of cattle. This would complete the 300 head that had been consigned to a buyer in Chicago a few months back. They had until the end of the week to get them penned and ready to move to the railhead in Marathon.

Federico could easily have stayed at his ranch. Lico was good at bossing a herd. His other boys and Valentín, who rode as pointers, were equally skillful at their jobs. There was just something about a roundup and cattle drive that got Federico's adrenaline flowing. He would make the rounds riding swing in back of the pointers, and sometimes even ride drag in the back with all the dust. His favorite spot was riding flank, rounding up the occasional stray. He would even take his turn at nighthawk. Nighthawks worked in teams of two with two-hour shifts throughout the night. They would circle the herd in opposite directions singing to the cattle to keep them calm, keep themselves awake and let the other rider know their whereabouts. The problem with Federico was that he was tone deaf. Each time he came close to the sleeping *vaqueros*, he would wake them with his off-key melodies. No one ever had the courage to tell him that he couldn't sing a lick. He knew it, but didn't care. Cattle didn't know any better.

Don Quixote

Sunday came. The men had returned in the middle of the night. Severita let Federico and his boys sleep in, preparing to serve a late breakfast. Regina, up at daybreak as was her custom, took the free time to read a book Miguel had given Severita some days before to keep her occupied in the men's absence. Regina had noticed the book lying next to the kerosene lamp Severita used to read at night. She read the first few chapters of the *Ingenious Hidalgo Don Quixote de la Mancha* by Miguel de Cervantes Saavedra. She was quickly captivated by the antics of Don Quixote and his squire, Sancho Panza. She was enthralled by the story of Kitri, who had bequeathed her love to Basilo, later to discover that her father has promised her to a foppish nobleman by the name of Gamache. Regina felt a certain kinship with Kitri. She was pained to put it down when Severita finally called her to the kitchen at mid-morning.

"I was reading the book Miguel gave you," Regina said. "Do you like it?"

"Very much."

"Take it to your room and finish reading it, if you like. I'll read it after you're done."

Federico walked in, catching the tail end of the conversation. "Read what?" he asked. He was returning from the horse trough outside that doubled as his bathtub every Sunday morning.

"A book that you would never take the time to read," Regina said.

"Which book is that?" Federico inquired.

"*Don Quixote de la Mancha.*"

"Have you gotten to the part where Quixote attacks the windmill?" her father asked with a big smile.

Federico's response stunned Regina. "You've read it?"

"*Mi hija*, in my youth, and in my home, all of Cervantes works were required reading."

After breakfast, the men rested and played dominoes. Jacobo and Valentín slipped away to go fishing as they did every Sunday, or so they would say. Where they would travel instead, was to Santa Elena across the river to pay and make arrangements for the week's consignment of clandestine liquor shipments. Santos knew where they were headed. He was paid well to help the boys conceal their ruse. Every so often, he would even go with Jacobo and Valentín and break off on his own to fish and wait while they took care of business. Whether Santos went with them or not, each somehow always managed to return with a tow sack full of catfish.

7

Fiesta

It was September of 1922. Plans were being made for the celebration of Mexican Independence Day on the 16th. The Villalba children were all born in the United States, but out of respect for their father and for their mother, they would join their parents in a lively commemoration of México's independence from Spain. Aside from New Year's Day, *Dia de los Tres Reyes*, Day of the Three Kings, and Sundays, it was the only time Federico would allow an interruption in the daily chores of the ranch. Some friends thought it odd that a man so proud of his Spanish heritage would find it important to celebrate the violent overthrow of Spanish rule. Federico celebrated the purging of the oppression of the *gachupines*, who exploited the wealth of the people and the country for more than three hundred years.

Colonial society had been highly stratified. Juan de Villalba, like others of Spanish birth, occupied the higher echelons. Second were *criollos*. Lower on the social rung were *mestizos*, the mixed blood of Spaniards and Native Mexicans and lowest were *indios y los africanos*.

Each socio-ethnic group had different privileges and responsibilities. Federico's grandfather, considered once removed from Spanish aristocracy, was treated as a second-class subject of the Spanish Crown. He and other disenchanted *criollos* ignited the flame of the Independence movement. Ramón, Federico's father, had taught his son to honor his Spanish heritage yet proclaim his *mejicanismo*, Mexican pride.

"Papá, who is going to give *el grito*, the cry of independence, this year?" Jacobo asked.

Federico smiled affectionately as he looked over to his youngest son. "*Santitos*," Federico said.

Miguel listened to the exchange with great interest. Talk of a celebration excited him. Considered an expert on the subject in his country, he was called upon to make a speech in Villa Unión in the central plaza every year on this special day.

"Don Federico, might I be able to say a few words during your celebration?" he asked.

"You want to make a speech?" Federico asked.

"If you would allow me the privilege," Miguel said.

"*¡Como no*, why not!" Federico exclaimed with a regal wave of his right hand.

A menu of *mole poblano, barbacoa* and the requisite complement of rice, beans, tortillas and biscuits was promised by Severita and her helpers. The day was set. Now all they needed was a shipment of illegal liquor. Jacobo volunteered to handle that particular detail.

The *fiesta* was a rousing success. The food was exceptional, the frivolity bounteous and the speech Miguel made impressive. Jacobo supplied an abundant and assorted supply of liquor. Santos, who had sneaked some *contrabando* behind the outhouse, gave a loud, somewhat slurred but very enthusiastic battle cry, "*¡Mejicanos! ¡Viva México! ¡Viva Independencia! ¡Viva la Virgen de Guadalupe!*"

After her father retired for the night, Regina, who had drunk her share of brandy, went over to congratulate Miguel on his speech.

"Did you like it?" he asked.

"Yes I did. You and my father seem to have much in common," she said.

"We don't agree on Pancho Villa," Miguel said, good-naturedly.

"Papá feels very strongly that Villa is an opportunist."

"How do you feel about Villa?"

"He is a shameless womanizer," Regina responded sharply. "My God, he has twenty-nine wives doesn't he?"

"Only two, but many girlfriends," Miguel said.

"There you have it!"

"Admittedly, he has a weakness for women, but he is a fearless man and a great general."

"Villa is what anyone wants him to be," Regina said. "It makes no difference to me," she added, summing up her opinion and at the same time making it clear she wanted to talk about something else.

As predicted, the Villalba boys, Valentín Baiza, his mother and father and several of his brothers, celebrated throughout the night, stopping only to wash up and change clothes as the morning sun greeted the horizon. The antidote for a night of revelry was a concoction called *ponche para los crudos*, punch for the hung over. The tonic, made with brown sugar, raisins, tamarind pods, prunes and preserved guava boiled in water and poured into a half of a glass of rum or brandy, accomplished one of two things; it either cured the sour stomach or purged it. Following the "hair of the dog" was the remedy's crowning touch, a hot bowl of *menudo* (tripe stew), which had cooked through the night. Though the medicinal qualities of this ritual were arguable, the belief in it was not. For a Villalba, the prospect of a hard day's work never spoiled a good night's *fiesta*.

The Baizas

Valentín's uncle and aunt, Pablo and Noné Baiza, were always welcome at the Villalba home and always invited to the celebrations. Noné Baiza and María had spent countless hours preparing meals for holidays and special events spanning twenty-five years of friendship.

Noné, nee Dodson, Baiza was born in 1881 on a ranch near Globe, Arizona, to Harve and Minnie Dodson. The family wandered into Terlingua Creek via Alpine that same year, settling in a remote area of the Chisos Mountains later referred to as Dodson Creek.

Harve built a one-room, 240-square-foot shanty with holes in the walls for windows and a dirt floor. His effort to shelter his family from the elements was commendable but inept. Harve Dodson was a goat rancher, not a builder. Wind, snow, rain and heat had little problem finding their way into the home. He pastured his goat herd some three miles from the homestead where he erected another clumsy structure. Made of willow logs and mud, it was home to his three teenage daughters who were assigned to tend the goats and protect them from bears that roamed the surrounding mountains and lower desert. The girls did a great job on both counts. Nary a goat was lost to the elements or to bears.

The second oldest of six boys, 31-year-old Pablo Baiza lived across the Río Bravo in Santa Elena. He and his older brother, Candelario, traveled to Study Butte for supplies once a month. On one of their trips, they overheard a conversation about Harve Dodson's teenage daughters who lived out on the range by themselves and tended his livestock. Once they found out exactly where the girls lived, they set out to find them.

The one thing they did not overhear back in the store was that the girls were well armed and very capable of defending themselves against uninvited visitors. Candelario and Pablo stumbled into the Dodson camp and three shotgun barrels that were perfectly capable of taking out two 400-pound black bears and would make quick work out of two 150-pound humans. Pablo apologized profusely for the intrusion and was successful in breaking through the girls' defenses.

One in particular took a shine to him. The men stayed to visit for a few hours. During a moment alone, 14-year-old Noné told Pablo that neither of her two older sisters liked Candelario. She asked Pablo to return, but next time without his brother and only to see her. Pablo returned time and again. He and Noné married a year later in 1897, one month past her sixteenth birthday much to the chagrin of her parents. Unfortunately, Noné did little to improve her lifestyle by marrying Pablo. The abject poverty she lived in on the U.S. side followed right along to the Mexican side and to Santa Elena.

Candelario Baiza had never been a friendly sort. He and Federico exchanged unkind words years back. Candelario's way of dealing with issues was always short-term, usually involving his guns, and on more than one occasion ending in someone's death. Though Federico never envisioned him as a threat to his own safety, he did see Candelario's actions as bringing unwanted attention to his family by mere association. He was tempted many times to fire Valentín and order his sons to stay away from any of Candelario's family, but always relented because of his fondness for the boy. He would settle for keeping eyes and ears trained on Candelario Baiza, always at the ready.

The Store

In Study Butte, Jorge, who had not attended the *fiesta*, was preparing for the day. He sat at the kitchen table enjoying his morning coffee with his wife and baby. Leaning forward on his elbows and cradling his cup of *cafécito* in both hands, he looked out the kitchen window.

"I imagine my brothers are having their *menudo* right about now, sitting there talking about the good time they had," he said.

"I wish you had gone," Golla said. "I know they missed you."

"Oh no," he said, shaking his head." Those days are long over for me. I have my family to consider, isn't that right my little ones?" he said, smiling first at his kids, then reaching across to his wife and gently pinching her cheek.

"Are you going to talk to your father about the store anytime soon?" Golla asked.

For the last few weeks, business had been at its worst ever. With all of the mine closures and with many families leaving the area, they had few customers.

Golla's question upset Jorge. "Papá doesn't need me to tell him that business is bad."

"Don't get angry with me, Chochi. I'm just wondering what our future holds. This affects our lives you know."

Jorge immediately regretted having been short with his wife. "I'm sorry, *mi amor*. You're right. I do need to talk to Papá. It can wait until tomorrow, Sunday."

Jorge and his family arrived early the next afternoon, hoping to speak with his father before the others gravitated to the main house. As luck would have it, Federico was on the porch enjoying his pipe and a cup of coffee. Severita and Regina were inside tending to the carving of a *javelina,* a wild pig the men had brought back with them and had cooked on the spit the better part of the morning.

"*¿Hola Papá, cómo les fué de fiesta?*" Jorge asked.

"It went well. Why didn't you join us?"

"Too much to do at the store. Besides, I don't trust myself around so much sotol."

Federico nodded and smiled. His demeanor then took on a more serious aspect.

"We're delivering 300 head to the railhead next week. Maybe you can help us on the drive," Federico said.

"*¡Seguro!*" Jorge hadn't been on a cattle drive in two years.

"*¡Traígame el niño!*" Federico hollered.

Golla stooped and gave her father-in-law the obligatory kiss on his cheek and handed him his grandson.

"Leave me the children," Federico said, setting his pipe aside and hoisting María to his lap.

Golla did as she was told. She excused herself and proceeded to the kitchen with infant, Elia in her arms to give Severita and Regina a hand.

"Papá, we need to talk about the store," Jorge said.

"Business is bad, I know," Federico said as he set his pipe aside and hoisted María onto his other knee and began bouncing both children. "*Caballito, caballito,*" he said, smiling at María's and Ruben's giggling.

"What are we going to do about it?"

"What do you propose we do?" Federico asked, continuing to play with his grandchildren.

"Close the store."

Federico stopped bouncing the children and looked at his son. "Why would we do that?"

Surprised at his father's reaction, words stuck in his throat.

"Papá, business..." Jorge found it impossible to assemble thoughts that would provide an answer for his father.

"These bad times could be temporary," Federico said. We'll reduce our inventory. The store is to remain open."

Christmas Traditions

The Christmas season arrived. It would be the family's fourth Christmas without Maria. As hard as Federico tried to nudge the family into the holiday spirit, they were all having great difficulty getting them past the memory of their mother. María's Yuletide spirit was legendary. The family's salvation was their deep Christian beliefs and the joy the Villalba grandchildren brought to the holidays. Perhaps his announcement later in the day would cheer the family up.

Golla helped Federico to get the others into the holiday mood. She had written Felipe, asking that he come down for Christmas with his wife and three children. He agreed and even brought a Christmas tree. It was the first to grace the Villalba adobe since

Maria's passing.

The Villalbas, unlike most other Mexican households, began their celebration on December 6 with the feast of *San Nicolás*.

The ancient pre-Christian Villalbas were from Alba, a city that was destroyed in 7 B.C. by the Romans, never to be rebuilt. Alba was in the region of Latium in central Italy, bordered by Tuscany, Umbria, Abruzzo, Molise, Campania and the Tyrrhenian Sea. Those who survived the war moved to Rome, where the Caelian hill was chosen as a home. It was then and there that the family became known as *Villa Alba* or House of Alba, later condensed to Villalba when family members adventured and settled in Sicily and eventually in the region of Lugo in Spain. Today, where Alba once stood, the town of Castel Gandolfo, the Pope's summer retreat, occupies the hills overlooking Lake Albano.

The charming Italian tradition of placing an empty plate on the table, where children left notes asking for gifts and promising to be good in the coming year had survived all of these many centuries. *San Nicolás* would fill the requests and leave chocolates, candies and other goodies for the children.

The Villalbas also celebrated *Las Posadas*, or The Inns, that begins on December 16 commemorating Mary and Joseph's journey into Bethlehem and their search for shelter. The children would also participate in the distribution of candy in town on Christmas Day. The month-long celebration would end on January 6, *el Día de Los Tres Reyes*, Day of the Three Kings, with the traditional gift exchange and the breaking of the *piñata*.

Felipe's children enjoying Christmas

The Announcement

Whether by plan or eventuality, Severita found her way into Federico's heart. Federico had given no thought to remarrying until Severita became such a big part of his life. Certainly, no one ever questioned Federico's love for María or his loneliness. No one openly objected to his announcement Christmas day that he and Severita would wed on January 6, 1923.

The Kiss

Miguel kept to himself for most of the day. He missed his family. He took solace in seeing the Villalbas celebrate Christmas in the truest spirit of the holy days. Yet he still felt out of place.

After her father announced his impending nuptials, Regina set out to look for Miguel. She last saw him talking to Lico on the other side of the dining room. She poked her head into the kitchen and saw that the door leading to the *ramada* was open. She went to the door and saw Miguel sitting outside alone.

Regina spoke first. "I'm pleased father has found love with Severita."

"It also pleases me," Miguel responded with a smile.

"Why aren't you inside with the others enjoying all of the food Severita and I made?" Regina asked.

"I feel like I'm an intruder," said Miguel.

"No such thing. You've worked for us for over a year now. How can you consider yourself an intruder?"

"You just said it, I've *worked* for you. I am an employee, not a family member or a long-time friend. I don't feel I belong."

"*Miguelito, no te me pongas nesio,* don't go acting like a child on me," Regina said.

"I don't mean to act childish. I just feel out of place."

Regina walked out to where Miguel was sitting and handed him a small box.

"What is this?" he asked, as he looked up at her in surprise.

"A present, what do you think?"

"But I didn't get you anything," he stammered.

"Yes you did," Regina replied.

"What was that?" he asked, with a perplexed look on his face.

"*Don Quixote*. I took it from Severita, and I'm not giving it back."

"You read it?"

"The first part."

"You liked it?"

"Every syllable."

"What did you get me?" he asked, hastily opening the well-wrapped box. "Oh Señorita, I cannot accept this. It is far too valuable," he said, admiring the gold medal of *La Virgen de Guadalupe* that gleamed beautifully in the moonlight.

"You must keep it or you will insult me. I have one other gift for you. Stand up and face me," she ordered. "Close your eyes."

Miguel did so dutifully. The next thing he felt were Regina's soft lips on his. His entire body shook with excitement. He steadied himself with a chair while he caught his breath and regained his composure.

"I've wanted that for a long time, but I wanted to do the kissing," he confessed.

"Well, now you can," Regina responded with a tenderness he had never heard in her voice before. Miguel took her hand and drew her to him. She melted against his chest.

The Wedding

Federico had the priest from the little mission in San Carlos brought up to officiate the wedding ceremony. He wanted a simple ceremony attended only by his children and Severita's relatives. Severita thought otherwise.

She was forty-nine and this was her first marriage. She'd always dreamed of a big wedding and a beautiful white wedding dress. She wanted friends to attend. She would settle for nothing less. They were married at the ranch of Severita's brother and Federico's good friend, Dolores. The ceremony and reception was attended by Federico's children and half the population of Terlingua.

The mariachis that Federico hired out of Alpine serenaded the wedding party. Beer and liquor flowed freely. The only complaint Severita had was that the reception was held next to the stables. Outside of that malodorous hitch, it was the wedding she'd always wanted.

The bride and groom and their best man and woman, Valentín and Jesusa Rodríguez, sat and watched the revelers dance. At the culmination of the ceremonial wedding dance where everyone took their turns dancing with the bride and groom, Federico picked up his bride, carried her outside to his horse and rode off with her to Rancho Barras to start their new life together.

Thanks to Severita, the last few years had yielded some sense of normalcy. Federico was very appreciative of Severita's devotion to his family. He vowed to himself to give her a good life. He hoped the harsh Big Bend country shared his sentiment. In the unforgiving desert, wishful dreams were sometimes like rainbows, ethereal and out of reach.

Defending Rancho Barras

Prickly pear flowers, prickly poppies and cholla cactus blossoms greeted April with its annual offering of delicate reds, whites and yellows. It was Federico's favorite season, in spite of the winds that visited the region this time of year. After dinner, Severita went out to the porch to deliver the week's mail that she and Regina had retrieved from Boquillas earlier in the day. Federico was leaning against a cedar post stoking his pipe one last time before exhaling a large puff of smoke to extinguish the match. He heard the screen door open and tiny footsteps approach him from behind.

"What do you have for me my love?" he said.

"Last week's mail and a cup of coffee." Severita answered.

"Aren't you going to join me?"

"Perhaps later. Right now, I've got to finish cleaning up the kitchen."

Federico relieved his wife of the thick stack of envelopes and the coffee. Severita smiled and walked back inside the house. Federico shuffled across the porch, boot heels sliding and clicking along the cracks between the planks as he made his way to his chair. He sat and sorted through the envelopes, looking to see which he would open first.

Regina joined her father on the porch after she finished helping Severita with the dishes. Severita stayed indoors to mend socks and britches.

"Have you finished the second part of *Don Quixote?*" Federico asked.

"I have. It was very entertaining. Cervantes writes so eloquently," Regina said.

"I have his *Novelas ejemplares* stowed away somewhere. Would you like to read them?"

"Oh, yes, that would be wonderful. Thank you, Papá."

"How are things between you and Severita?"

"She's a nice lady. We get along alright."

"*Mi hija*, I am planning a train trip to Chihuahua next month. Severita and I would like for you to join us. It will give you and Francisco an opportunity to spend some time together."

Those were the last words Regina wanted to hear out of her father's mouth.

"Papá, I've been meaning to talk to you about Francisco."

Federico turned and looked at his daughter. "What about Francisco?"

"What he and I had is ancient history. I don't feel the same about him."

"That's exactly why I want you to go," Federico said. "You two don't see each other often enough. He's busy on his father's ranch. You're busy here. You and Francisco need time alone. I've already arranged it with Juan. He's promised to give Francisco free time to spend with you.

"*Por favor, Papá*, don't make me go," Regina pleaded.

"You'll enjoy yourself. You'll see," he said.

There was no use arguing. The decision had been made. Regina knew she could say or do nothing to change his mind.

The Engagement Test

Regina was having great difficulty finding the words to tell Miguel that she would go to Chihuahua City to see Francisco. She was most troubled by the realization that deep down inside, she wanted to go. She met her fiancé for the first time three years earlier when her father's cousin, Juan Villalba, his wife Tomasa and their five boys visited Rancho Barras. They stayed for two weeks. The children struck up a wonderful friendship and were inseparable during the two-week stay. They promised each other that they would persuade their parents to allow them to get together again that summer. It took some convincing, but Regina won over her parents, and they let her accompany Lico and Jacobo to Chihuahua.

Francisco, the middle son, was two years Regina's senior. During the most recent summer trip, their relationship began to change. Francisco and Regina were always looking for opportunities to sneak off together. It was apparent that the two were becoming more than just playmates. On one occasion, Santos followed the couple to the back of the barn. He hid behind the chicken coop and through a knothole saw Francisco embrace and kiss Regina. Later, Santos confronted his sister, who admitted she was in love with *Panchito* (Francisco's nickname). She swore Santos to secrecy. He never told a soul.

Regina and Santos' pact was all for naught. It was difficult for Francisco and Regina to hide their feelings for one another. During that fateful summer, Juan noticed furtive glances between the two, and the way his son would brush up against Regina when he thought no one was looking. He finally took his son aside and asked him about his relationship with Regina. Francisco confessed that they had fallen in love. Juan immediately sent word to Federico and María asking that they come to Chihuahua so that they might discuss this development.

Federico was fond of Francisco. When he would come to Rancho Barras, the young man would work side by side with his boys. All along he thought Francisco was visiting to be with his boys, when all he wanted was to be close to Regina. Now that the relationship was in the open, Francisco would have to keep a respectable distance. The only way the two could continue their relationship was if Regina were betrothed to Francisco.

In addition, they could only be together under the watchful eye of either set of parents. Regina was never again allowed to go to Chihuahua for a visit without at least one parent in tow. The lovers were never permitted to be alone again.

There were long months between visits. The magic that Regina and Francisco once shared had become only a warm memory. Regina now had strong feelings for Miguel. Were they strong enough to survive the trip to Chihuahua? She would find out soon enough.

Regina poked her head into her father's study where Miguel was working on her father's books. "Do you have a moment?" she asked.

"Of course." Miguel put down his pencil and motioned for her to come in and sit in the chair next to the desk.

Regina settled into the chair and pointed to a pair of six and twelve-pointers on the wall to her left.

"See those deer antlers up there?"

"Yes. What about them?"

"Those are my trophies."

Miguel glanced at the antlers briefly, and then looked back at Regina. "Wonderful, but I know you didn't come in here to talk about your hunting prowess. What is it you want?"

"My parents are taking me to Chihuahua next month."

Miguel paused for a moment before responding. "That should be a pleasant trip this time of year."

It wasn't the response Regina expected. "You don't understand. We will be staying with Francisco and his parents at his ranch," she explained.

"I thought as much."

"Doesn't that bother you?" Regina asked, miffed that he was sitting there so impassively.

"It does, but there is not much I can do about it, is there?"

"Aren't you the least bit jealous?"

"I'm feeling a bit insecure, but I'm not jealous," he said. "You've had a long-standing relationship with Francisco. For God's sake, he's your fiancé."

"In name only. I don't care for him anymore," Regina interrupted.

Miguel sighed and clasped his hands.

"Let's be honest. You and I have known each other for all of seven months. Francisco has been in your life far longer. How can I expect to compete and win under these circumstances?"

Regina looked at Miguel angrily. "I'm not a prize someone competes for."

"I'm sorry; I didn't mean to infer that you were anyone's prize. Regina, the truth is I care for you a great deal, but I am painfully aware that you are promised to another. Look, just go—enjoy yourself—what happens, happens."

Regina was uncharacteristically silent. She searched for words that would allow Miguel to feel more secure in their relationship.

"I'll go, but I doubt I'll have a good time. I'd rather stay here with you."

Miguel smiled and nodded. "I appreciate the sentiment."

Regina got out of her chair, looked behind her to see that no one was at the door and went over to Miguel to kiss him on the forehead. She left the room without either saying anything more.

8

Smuggling Liquor

Jacobo and Valentín made their weekly jaunt to Santa Elena. Valentín seemed especially quiet. "Valentín, what's bothering you?" he asked as they approached the Río Grande shoreline.

"My father has become stubborn," Valentín confided.

"He still wants in the business, does he?"

"He's making my life miserable. He's threatening to tell your father about the bootlegging if we don't cut him in."

Jacobo shrugged. "We'll let them in," he said.

"Are you sure, *manito?*" Valentín asked, surprised Jacobo had given in so quickly.

"We could use the help. Our orders have quadrupled since we started the business. As long as Candelario and Pablo understand they work for us, I don't see a problem. Do you?"

"Not so much with Pablo, but with my father, *si!*"

"It will be alright. Our business partners are loyal to us. Even if your father got greedy and had the *cojones,* to try and horn in on our suppliers or our clients, they would never do business with him. They would have hell to pay, if they did."

"You're probably right," Valentín said. He knew Cobito to be wiser beyond his years and very brave. He also knew his father to be ruthless.

Jacobo could see the apprehension on Valentín's face.

"Don't worry, brother. I'll handle your father."

Jacobo and Valentín increased their bootleg deliveries tenfold. Interestingly enough, their new co-workers, Candelario and Pablo Baiza, proved to be valuable assets to the business, at least for the time being. The elder Baizas bragged at how they were able to befriend and bribe several of the "vigilantes" into allowing unrestricted access both ways.

When Jacobo asked how, Candelario replied, "We promised them money and drink."

"*Diablos* or customs officers?" Jacobo asked. "Neither. They are civilian dummies that were recruited to help," Pablo said.

How can you be sure they will not turn on us?" Jacobo asked.

"I told them that if they did not cooperate, I would kill them," Candelario answered smugly.

Candelario and Pablo brought an effective but dangerous element to the business. Jacobo planned to keep a tight rein on the two through the course of their business relationship.

Regina Listens to Her Heart

Regina began packing for her trip to Chihuahua. They would leave early in the morning. She and Miguel had spent wonderful moments together since her announcement. She was fond of him but honestly did not know how things would fare when she finally saw Francisco again. They hadn't corresponded in months and hadn't seen each other since her mother's passing. Regina's thoughts were interrupted by a light knock on the door.

"¿*Quién es?*"

"Severita."

"*Pasele.*"

"I've wanted to talk to you," Severita said, as she closed the door behind her.

Regina finished folding a nightgown and put it in her satchel. "About what?" Regina asked.

"Your father knows about you and Miguel."

"He does? How?"

"The mesquite has eyes and ears," Severita said with a blink of the eye and a knowing nod of the head.

"What has he said?"

"He's ready to fire Miguel, and he's very disappointed with you," Severita confided.

"Is that why he planned the trip?"

Severita nodded her head again.

Regina sat on the bed next to her stepmother.

"I think I'm in love with Miguel," she confessed as she folded her hands in her lap.

"You no longer have any feelings for Francisco?" Severita asked.

"That's just it. I don't know. I have wonderful memories." Regina paused and reflected for an extra moment. "What we had was truly amazing. I honestly can't tell you what I'm going to feel when I see Francisco again," she said.

"Well, you know what your father expects to happen," Severita said.

"Yes, I know," she sighed.

A long moment passed before either spoke. Regina looked across her shoulder at Severita and pleaded. "Please tell father not to fire Miguel."

"I've already made that appeal, but you know as well as I do, there is no single person who influences your father when it comes to business decisions."

"But this isn't a business decision," Regina snapped.

"From his standpoint it is." It pained Severita to put her husband in a bad light, but it had to be said. It was the truth.

Lico deposited his father, Severita and Regina at the train depot in Alpine early Saturday morning. It would be the first time his father had left the ranch since their fateful trip to Allende. Federico was far more apprehensive about his impending absence than his boys were. As much as they loved their father, a two-week respite from his firm hand was a welcome relief.

"*Mi hijo*, make certain to contact me if any emergency presents itself," Federico said.

"*Si Papá*. We'll send you a telegram. Don't worry about a thing. You go have a good time," he said.

The conductor hurried around the slower moving Villalbas as he made his way down the boardwalk announcing the train's impending departure to El Paso. "All aboard!" he yelled through a short stubby megaphone, skillfully weaving his way through the crowd.

The steam engine coughed and snorted, ready to pull its load through the beauty of the mesas, canyons, mountains and deserts of the Trans-Pecos region.

The three boarded the Pullman and settled into their berths. Severita slid in and sat next to Regina while Federico's attention was devoted to stowing their satchels in the overhead compartment. Federico looked down, wondering why his wife chose to sit with Regina.

"Aren't you going to sit with me?" Federico asked.

"*Al momento, no*," Severita said. From comments Federico had made to her in passing, she expected her husband would not wait long to bring up the subject of Miguel. Severita felt Regina might appreciate having someone at her side when it came time to defend her feelings for the schoolteacher. The coach jerked forward as the engineer let go of the brake.

On the antelope plain east of Marfa, Federico asked his daughter to put down her book. "Regina, I understand you and Miguel have a relationship."

Regina took a deep breath before placing the book in her lap.

"I am very fond of Miguel, if that is what you are asking."

"Fond, what does the word fond mean? One is fond of a pet—fond of a book. What do you mean by fond?" Federico asked.

"I like him very much. Papá, I love him," she said, finally admitting her true feelings for Miguel.

"I see. What of Francisco? How can you throw away your relationship with him for a total stranger?"

"There is no longer any relationship with Francisco. We haven't communicated in some time. He has yet to answer a letter I sent him from Fort Davis, months ago," Regina said, hoping to buttress her case.

Federico would have none of it.

"I am not going to allow you to throw away a wonderful future with a man that can give you the life you deserve for some scrawny, crippled school teacher."

"How dare you talk about Miguel in that manner," Regina said. "He has been a hard-working and loyal employee to you. He has done everything you've asked of him and more. Miguel doesn't deserve your disrespect. Besides, you already have me married to Miguel. Who has said anything about marriage?"

Federico and Regina were both strong willed. Severita knew neither would give any ground. It was time to end the argument.

"Federico, let this situation take its course. If it is meant for Regina and Francisco to be together, it will happen. How can you possibly think you can force your daughter to love someone over another?" Severita asked.

"Love is only part of this," Federico said.

"What other part is there to this, business perhaps?" Severita asked. "Are you more concerned about the business end of your daughter's relationships than you are with her feelings?"

"Of course not. I love my daughter. I want what's best for her."

"That's what I hoped you would say," Severita said. "Be there for Regina if she asks for your guidance, but let her decide who to love. Federico, you are a wise man. I once heard you say, 'Love is its own master.' I believe you said that we could 'not control its arrival or its intent; all we could do was abide by its sentiment and revel in its willingness and eagerness to occupy the heart.' Do I remember correctly?" she asked.

"Yes, that's what I said," Federico conceded. "That doesn't mean I have to love the man she chooses."

Severita shook her head in mild frustration. "Federico, *eres imposible.*"

Regina could never have disarmed her father the way Severita had. It was a welcome development that she took full advantage of. She quickly returned to reading her book. Nothing more was said about Francisco or Miguel for the balance of the trip.

Regina and Francisco

When Federico and his family arrived at the ranch, Juan and Tomasa greeted him warmly and apologetically.

"I'm sorry Francisco is not here with us to welcome you. He is in the city taking care of family business," Juan explained.

Juan was lying. He had no idea where his son was. He had left on family business the day previous and had not returned.

Regina was embarrassed and angry at her fiancé's absence. She remained silent letting her father handle the matter.

Federico introduced his wife. He chose not to comment on Francisco's absence. It was clear he wasn't happy about the circumstance. It upset him to know that his cousin had no control over his son.

Juan had the maid show Federico and his family to their rooms. Judging from Federico's reaction, he had some ruffled feathers to smooth over.

Regina sat in her room feeling emotionally drained. She had suffered the indignity of her father forcing her to come on this trip, and now the humiliation of her fiancé's absence. She tried taking her mind off her troubles by reading her book while her parents rested from the trip. She was tired out, more even than she had thought; the words lulled her to sleep. She was suddenly awakened by the voice of two men in the courtyard. They were well into an argument outside her window. Once she was awake enough to distinguish the voices, she could tell it was Francisco and his father. She thought better than to go to the window to spy on them. She sat in her chair, listening.

"You have embarrassed me beyond comprehension," she heard Don Juan say loudly.

"I am sorry, Papá. I will personally apologize to Don Federico and his family."

"I fully expected you would. What about Regina?" Juan asked.

"What about her, Papá? She is here. We will talk and come to an understanding. I don't understand your concern. This is my life, not yours."

"You talk to her. You tell her how much of a *sin vergüenza*, shameless one, you were for not having had the common decency to be here to greet her and her parents. And you be sure and tell Federico and his wife that I did not raise you to be *malcreado*, unmannerly," he demanded.

Francisco smiled. "I will, Papá, *cálmate*. You're going to give yourself a heart attack," he said, trying to bring some levity to the situation.

Juan would have none of it and walked away in frustration.

Regina thought there might be similar dynamics between Francisco and his father as there were between her and her *papá*. This made the situation all the more curious. While freshening up at the water basin, Regina heard a light rap on the door.

"Señorita Villalba, dinner is served," the maid announced.

"I'll be right there," she said, dabbing the moisture off her face with the embroidered linen towel that she found next to the pitcher and basin.

The large monogrammed V in the corner reminded her of the enormous pride the Villalbas had in their name and heritage. She remembered at one time thinking that if she were to marry Francisco, she would not have to change her surname. At the time, it seemed like a novel compromise.

Francisco looked at Regina as she entered the dining room and was again overwhelmed by her beauty and carriage. She was as proud a woman as he had ever met. The remorse he felt for not having been home to greet her earlier suddenly overwhelmed him. He walked over to her and escorted her to the table, asking permission to sit next to her. She waited a respectable moment before consenting, insisting he sit to her left. It was her way of letting him know that she was upset with him.

The complement of polite conversation at dinner dared not approach any topic that might incite any more tension. After dinner, Francisco asked Regina and then Federico for permission for her to accompany him to the courtyard. It seemed the courtyard was the place of choice for volatile discourse.

Regina spoke as they approached the courtyard. "Saddle up the horses," she demanded.

"Do what?" he asked, thinking he had not heard her correctly.

"I said saddle up the horses. We are going for a ride."

"But you're wearing a dress," Francisco pointed out.

"And what does that have to do with anything?" Regina asked.

Francisco knew better than to argue with Regina. He quickly disappeared into the stable while Regina sat in the courtyard enjoying the smell of the jasmine vines that adorned the pillars of the gazebo.

"Here we are," he said, smiling at Regina, with reins and horses trailing behind each hand. Regina stopped him short as he came over to help her onto the horse.

"*Quítate*, remove yourself," she ordered. "I can mount the horse myself." Regina put her foot in the stirrup and skillfully pulled herself and her long skirt up onto the saddle.

"Forgive me for not having been here when you arrived," Francisco said as they rode out towards the trail they had taken many times before.

"Where were you?" she asked.

"I was drinking with my friends in town. I had a bit too much, and I lost track of time and my senses."

"Are you sure you weren't with your girlfriend and just didn't want to leave her to come and see me?"

"It was nothing like that. You are the only woman I have ever loved," he declared. "The truth is when my father told me you were coming, I didn't know what I was going to say to you about not writing or not coming to see you."

"You abandoned me," she said, her eyes never leaving Francisco's.

Perhaps if Francisco would have continued being attentive, their relationship might have continued to withstand the miles of separation. The anger she felt was turning into hurt.

"Why didn't you just write and tell me that you didn't love me anymore?"

"Because that would not have been true," he answered. "I do love you and miss you terribly. That is the quandary I am in. I also love my country. I would not want to live anywhere else.

"You've made it very clear to me that you would never join me in México. Each time we see each other, our time together is glorious and then you or I leave. It is always months before we see each other again. It's insane to continue this way!"

Wishing for inspiration, Regina looked up at the full moon. The anguish in Francisco's voice disarmed her. Whatever anger she felt melted into empathy.

"*Amores de lejos solo para los pendejos,* long-distance romances are solely for the dummies," she quipped, glancing at Francisco with a smile.

Francisco smiled at Regina's quirky, poignant riposte. He truly admired and loved her. As much as he wanted her, he knew she would never be his.

"Can I kiss you?" Francisco asked.

Without uttering a word, Regina stopped her horse and dismounted. Francisco followed her lead and met her in the middle of the trail. Silhouetted by the moonlight, Francisco removed his *sombrero* and gently pulled Regina to him. He lowered his face to hers and kissed her passionately.

They would live and love in the moment, and for the next two weeks enjoy each other's company and reminisce about what they once had. Though the thought of Miguel was on her mind and in her heart, his name was never mentioned.

When she kissed Francisco the night before she left for the Big Bend, they both knew it would be for the last time.

As Juan's driver took them to the train depot, Regina announced her breakup with Francisco to her father and Severita. Federico appeared disturbed but said nothing. The announcement came as no surprise to Severita. Little more was said for the entire trip home.

9

Regina and Miguel

Federico was pleasantly surprised to see Jorge and his little family at the Alpine train station to greet them. He was especially pleased to see his grandchildren.

"What a delightful sight," he said, smiling.

"How was the trip?" Jorge asked. Federico was busy playing with the baby. Regina was in no mood to talk. Severita took the initiative.

"Agreeable."

Jorge stowed the luggage in the steamer trunk strapped to the back of his Model A. He tied his father's duster coat and the blankets they took for the train ride with a rope to the top of the trunk much like he would tie bedding on a saddle.

"*Listo*," he said once he was done, signaling everyone to pile into the car.

"Looks like you got a little rain," Federico said, surveying the countryside with a wide sweep of his head.

"A little, but not enough," Jorge said.

Ordinarily, the Big Bend received about twelve inches of rain per year. So far, they had gotten half of that, with only a few months to make up the difference.

"Papá, Mr. Ed Gleim came by the store the other day."

"What did he want?"

"He didn't really say. All he told me was that he wanted to talk to you. I told him to go see you at the ranch after you returned."

"How's business?" Federico asked.

There was noticeable disappointment in Jorge's voice. "No better. And you, little sister, how did it go?"

Regina hadn't uttered a word since they had arrived.

"I had fun," she said.

Severita asked Jorge and his family to stay for dinner as they pulled up to the ranch house. Santos, Lico and Jacobo appeared from the bunkhouse where they were playing poker with several of the *vaqueros*. They had absolutely no regret about separating the *vaqueros* from their hard earned cash over a good game of cards.

"*¡Bienvenidos!*" Jacobo yelled from across the courtyard.

Regina noticed that when the boys looked at her directly their faces suddenly took on what appeared to be a look of sadness. She thought it odd. Lico pulled Regina aside as the rest of the family made their way into the house.

"I have something for you," he said, handing her a sealed envelope with her name on the outside. She recognized Miguel's handwriting.

"Where is he?" she asked.

"Read the letter," Lico said.

She opened it, wary of its contents.

My Dearest Regina,

I apologize that I was not here to greet you. I have returned to Villa Unión. As much as I dreamed of taking you into my arms upon your return, I feared that you would remain in the arms of Francisco. It was then I realized that I had no right to breach your relationship with your fiancé. I never heard from your lips that you did not love him. I could not bear to think that your affection for me might only be an apparition of your love for him. I thought it best to absence myself from your life, with the longing that I might be wrong. I beg that you not be angry. As I have become aware that your father knows of our relationship, should you decide to write, I will send my correspondence to Golla and will address it to Margarita [Daisy] the name of your favorite flower. By this method, if my letter ever falls into the hands of your father, you will not suffer the embarrassment of having to explain the letter, or my intentions. Please know that I care for you deeply, and I pray that I hear back from you.

Sinceramente,

Miguelito

After reading the letter, Regina had tears in her eyes. She was unaware that her brother had only removed himself to the darkness of the porch. He had stayed behind to console her.

"I'm sorry, *manita*," Lico said. "We tried convincing him to stay, but he insisted on going home. He didn't want to come between you and *Panchito*."

"There is no *Panchito*," Regina said. "We are no more."

After a discomfited moment of silence, Lico said, "That's good for Miguel—no?"

"I don't know yet." Regina sighed. She was truly disappointed that Miguel was not here for her return. Did his leaving have a purpose beyond what he wrote? Regina knew her mind. She had just ended a long-distance relationship. Why entertain the prospect of another?

"We'll see," she said, reaching into her drawstring purse. She pulled out a handkerchief and dabbed the corner of her eyes. Once again she felt abandoned.

Quickly the letter slipped into her purse; she then took a deep breath and walked inside. It would be six months before Regina finally wrote to Miguel. His long wait boiled down to flagellation, his penance for wandering off alone.

10

Hard Times

Ed Gleim came to Rancho Barras to visit with Federico. The two sat on the porch and shared a freshly opened bottle of French cognac.

"Fred, I think we need to join up the Texas Almaden store and your Study Butte store if we're going to stay in business," Ed said.

"I'm not sure I understand what you're driving at," said Federico.

"You might remember, a while back I hired a fella' by the name of Dan Coffman to run the store and another fella' to guard the mine."

Federico shook his head, "no," as he drew on his pipe.

"No matter. Anyway, Coffman tells me he's quittin' and going back to his farm in Shafter. Wanted to leave before Thanksgivin', but I talked him into waitin' until after the first of the year."

"What does that have to do with me?" Federico asked.

"I thought maybe you could shut down your place and move yer inventory over t' mine," Gleim proposed.

"How would that benefit me?" Federico asked.

Ed Gleim knew Federico to be a practical man. The question didn't surprise him; as a matter of fact, he half-expected it.

"It's not going to make us a bunch of money," Gleim said. Hell, I'm doing mostly credit business, and I know you are too. Maybe by cuttin' our operatin' costs in half, both of us can stay open, at least 'til things get better. If we both wind up shuttin' down, your people won't have anybody to turn to. What do you think?"

"Let me think about it. Now let's you and I pay proper attention to this bottle I have here," Federico said, refilling his friend's glass.

As promised, Federico gave the idea some thought. At the moment, it didn't seem all that appealing to him. If conditions worsened, he'd give it additional thought but for now, he'd leave things the way they were.

The Mines and Mexican Workers

The biggest employer in the Big Bend was the mining industry. There are no reliable records of mercury production before 1919. Production from 1919 to 1941 inclusive was 55,081 flasks. The Chisos Mining Company produced 39,094 flasks; the Rainbow Mine produced 8,087 flasks. The Big Bend and Texas Almaden produced 4,554 and 417 flasks, respectively. The Maríscal Mine produced 484 flasks from 1919 to 1923. Nine other mines produced 1,905 flasks during the twenty-two years. Many of the mines shut down in 1907 when the worldwide economy took a nosedive, but the Chisos, with its deep pockets, was able to remain open. The significantly reduced peacetime demand for mercury did, however, cause the mine to shut down its recently installed rotary furnace, relying on a 22-ton Scott furnace. Howard Perry, who had once paid himself as much as $40,000 per year, exclusive of the hundreds of thousands of dollars he realized in annual profit, was now down to paying himself $10,000 per year. Though he had to tighten his belt, the economic downturn by no means made him a pauper.

The Chisos store, which had been a gem of Perry's holdings in the Big Bend, was also struggling. In a letter to Perry, Cartledge asked Perry if he could extend credit to the Mexican employees who were struggling to make ends meet. Perry responded:

> *My dear Robert: No, we are not going to give the Mexicans credit. They can get along while we are shut down. They will have to help one another. The Company has practically supported that Big Bend Country for two years while it made no money, and now [it's] losing money. We are not going to let the Mexicans get into us. We not only want to save our money, but as soon as any Mexican or Mexicans have got into us then we will be obliged to hire them to get even. We are not going to have our hands tied in any such fashion.*

Chisos Company Store

Anglo mine employees, other mining companies and a select few local ranchers received store credit. Robert Cartledge wrote to Alpine rancher T. J. Roberts, who was delinquent on a note he had signed as an arrangement to make payments on an overdue store account:

Your note became due on May 1st. However, to date we have failed to here [sic] from you with remittance. As I told you… we would at least expect Interest and parcial [sic] payment on this note. Tho [sic] we would like to help you all possible [sic], at same time, we feel before that we have helped you consider-able by carring [sic] account so long before we had you make a note. At time we allowed credit, we…did same thru wanting to help all possible ranch men. Hoping to receive at least interest and part on note by early mail, we beg to remain.

Robt. Cartledge

Perry's capitalist disregard for the very people that had made him millions of dollars spoke volumes.

The Coffman Boys

These were lean times. Even the bootleggers were feeling the pinch. Fortunately for the cattle ranchers, the Midwest was still buying beef, and the Villalbas were kept busy supplying.

Regina and Miguel corresponded regularly. Miguel and his brother Antonio had bought the property in Ciudad Acuña, as they had planned. Miguel made plans to visit Regina in the spring. The Villalba store was still operational, but just barely. Federico's saddlery business was the only reason their doors were able to remain open.

Ed Gleim approached Federico once again about joining forces because Dan Coffman was leaving soon. Federico stuck to his guns.

At Coffman's suggestion, Gleim hired Coffman's 19-year-old son, Winslow, to take his father's place. Dan stuck around to show his son the ropes. Gleim had let go the elder Coffman's assistant, J. B. Huntley, with the anticipation that the young man would handle both jobs; Winslow didn't want any part of staying alone. He appealed to his father to ask Gleim if he could hire his younger brother, Aubrey "Jack", who was eighteen, to guard the mine and keep him company.

Against his better judgment, Gleim relented and hired Winslow's kid brother. It wasn't too long after Dan's departure that the undisciplined and now unrestrained Coffman boys began to stir up trouble.

A few days later, Federico sent Jacobo into Study Butte to pick up some feed from the store. Jorge welcomed his little brother with an invitation to stay for dinner.

"We're having your favorite, *chile colorado*," Jorge announced.

"Great! You don't have to invite me twice," Jacobo said.

"You ever meet Dan Coffman's boys over at the Texas Almaden?"

"No, not yet. Isn't one about your age? I think his name is Winslup, or some funny name like that."

"Hell, I don't know. I'm just wondering if we're not passing up on some *tiernitos* (rookies) for poker," Jacobo said with a smile.

"Perhaps," Jorge said, grinning.

"Why don't we go over after dinner and size them up?" Jacobo suggested.

Santos (with unidentified child) and Jacobo Villalba

Hooking the Rookies

After dinner, the two Villalba boys rode over to the Almaden store and introduced themselves to Jack and Winslow. After a bit of small talk, Jacobo cast the bait.

"You fellas like to play cards?" he asked.

Jack answered. "Some...why, there a card game somewhere?"

"This Saturday, as a matter of fact, over at *La Fiesta*," Jorge said.

"Don't have much money," Jack said.

"Don't worry, we only play for pennies," Jacobo assured Coffman.

"Sure, we'll be there. What time?"

"About seven. Bring your own liquor. They don't sell it in town. If you don't, I'll have sotol there for $2 a bottle," Jacobo said.

The Villalbas left feeling confident that the Coffmans were easy marks.

"*Manito*, Papá still has no idea that you're running liquor?" Jorge asked his little brother.

"If he does, he hasn't let on."

"What are you doing with all of the money, Cobito?"

"I've got it in a bank in Santa Elena."

"What good is it doing there?" Jorge asked.

"It's there if Papá or any of the family ever needs it," Jacobo said.

"You know as well as I do that Papá would never take that money knowing where it came from."

"I'll tell him I won it in a card game," Jacobo said, laughing.

"That much money? It would have to have been one hell of card game," Jorge joked. "The only one around here that has that kind of money is *El Perro*.

"There you go. The next time *El Perro* comes to Terlingua, I'll tell Papá that I goaded him into a card game and beat him with a royal flush."

Jorge shook his head and laughed. "What are we going to do with you, Cobito?"

Jacobo Buys a Ranch

Jacobo and Valentín had finished their business in Santa Elena and were having lunch at their favorite café when Jacobo spoke up.

"You know Valentín, Jorge's right. My father would never accept any money from me," he said, leaning into the bottle of *cerveza* he held by its neck. "Perhaps the best thing to do is to invest it."

"How?" Valentín asked.

"I buy a ranch, here in Santa Elena." Jacobo said. "You want in?"

"I wish I could. Papá spends my money as fast as I make it," Valentín said. He quickly shook off the disappointment and asked, "How do you propose to run the place? We're only here one day a week."

"I'll hire someone to run it for me."

Valentín shook his head. "I don't know, brother. It would have to be someone you could trust."

"It's not impossible, we'll find someone, you'll see."

"I think it's a crazy idea, but if anybody can make it work, you can."

"All right then—let's put the word out."

By the following week, Jacobo heard a rancher was selling 200 hectares that ran along San Carlos Creek, along with 300 head of cattle. He visited Don Santiago, the old man selling a ranch called *Los Fuegos.* He fell in love with the property and bought it. The acquisition was bittersweet.

He had acquired a ranch on his own, and before his twentieth birthday, but he could not share the accomplishment with his father. It would be a secret from the man he most admired, loved and respected.

The Card Game

Saturday night came. As planned, Lico and Jacobo came by and picked up Jorge and drove over to the Villalba family *cantina, La Fiesta*. Because of the Volstead Act, no liquor was sold at the *cantina*. Federico sold *botanas*, snacks and pop. He allowed his customers to bring their own liquor. The Coffmans were there waiting for them, and from what they could see, they were well into the bottle of sotol they most likely bought from one of the local bootleggers.

"Didn't think you boys were going to show up," Jack said.

"We're ten minutes early," Jorge replied.

"Yeah, but you Mesicans say seven when you really mean six, because you assholes are always showing up late," Jack mumbled.

"What is this *pendejo* saying?" Jacobo asked Lico.

Afraid that his brother would lose his temper, Lico downplayed the exchange.

"Don't pay attention to him," Lico said, shaking his head.

"Stop talking and start playing," Jacobo ordered.

Jacobo made his way to the table in the farthest corner from the saloon doors. The others followed. Jacobo never liked having his back to a door. He always wanted full view of the room.

"Okay, 10-cent ante, pair of jacks to open, three raise maximum, maximum bet $5," Lico said.

"I thought you said you played for pennies," Winslow said.

"We do, but for the people with good hands and *cojones*, the stakes are there if you want them. If you don't have them, don't bet them. Any objections?" Jacobo asked.

"I guess not," the older Coffman said.

The Villalba boys let the Coffmans win a few hands. As

expected, they started betting heavier on so-so hands. Jacobo quickly was up $20.

Jorge didn't want to take advantage of the two young men, especially Jack who'd been drinking most of the sotol. He suggested calling it a night. Jack would have no part of it. They continued playing. As the night progressed, Jorge's luck began turning. He took a $50 pot with a king high straight flush, the biggest of the night. Of that, $25 was Jack Coffman's. Jack was down to his last $2. Winslow had tapped out ten hands back. Jack surveyed Jorge's pile that looked to be about $80.

"How about one last hand for all ya' got in front of you," he said to Jorge.

Jorge looked at Jack quizzically. "You don't have enough money to cover that bet,"

"I've got a truck outside worth at least $150. I'll put that up. How's that?" Jack asked.

"I don't think so," Jorge said, gathering in his money.

"You chicken, Mesican?"

Jacobo erupted. "You call us Mesican one more time and you're dead where you sit!"

Jorge quickly intervened. "Look, young man you've had a little too much to drink, and I don't want to take advantage of you," Jorge warned.

"One card, highest card wins," Jack demanded, paying little attention to Jorge.

Jorge looked at Jack for a long moment, then he looked over at Jacobo and finally at Lico.

"It's up to you, brother," Lico said.

"Okay, Lico deals," Jorge declared.

"That's fine with me," Jack answered. Lico shuffled the cards for longer than he normally would, and then gave the cards to Jack to cut. Jack tapped the top of the cards with his knuckles. Lico dealt Jack the top card and his brother the next.

"You first," Jack said.

Jorge flipped over the queen of hearts. *"La reina del amor,* the queen of love," Jorge said.

Jack briskly rubbed the bottom of the card back and forth on the table before flipping it over.

"Ten of spades," Jacobo said.

"I know what it is, *Mes-i-can.* I'm not blind," Jack shouted angrily. "You three cheated. I know you did."

He started to reach for a gun he had in his waistband in back and underneath his vest.

"I don't think so, *señor.*"

Jack suddenly felt two barrels against the back of his head and knew the *cantinero* had a shotgun in his hands.

"No problem," Jack said, bringing his hand into plain sight and raising it and his other hand, above his head.

"Now, you slowly reach into your pocket, take out the keys to Jorge's truck, put them on the table and get the hell out my bar. You understand, *gringo?*" the *cantinero* said.

Jack swallowed hard. "Perfectly."

Winslow had no weapon and no desire to die. He raised his hands and followed behind Jack as they ran through the swinging doors.

"I shouldn't have taken that kid's truck," Jorge said.

"He lost it fair and square," said Jacobo.

After a good look around to make sure Jack wasn't lying in wait, the Villalbas exited the bar. Jacobo and Lico dropped Jorge off at home."

"You want us to stick around?" Jacobo asked.

"No. You two get on home. I'll be okay. I'll sleep with one eye open," Jorge said. "Besides, the kid's probably home changing his drawers after the scare Benito gave him."

Unequal Justice

Jack Coffman was embarrassed and fuming at what had happened. He was convinced the Villalbas had somehow cheated him out of his truck. Even at that, he thought, how can I tell my father that I was dumb enough to bet the family truck in a card game? On the long walk back to Terlingua, he spotted a Mexican gentleman who also appeared to be *borachito*.

"Where ya' going, Mesican?" Jack yelled.

"*A mi casa*," the farmer said, innocently.

"Ya know you Mesicans are stupid and a bunch of cheatin' bastards!" Jack shouted, walking closer.

The farmer was unarmed and frightened. He could see the young man was infuriated. Though he had no idea what Jack was rambling on about, he took the high road and apologized. "*Perdóneme, señor.*"

Jack reached around his back and retrieved his gun. "I oughta' shoot your ass right here!" Jack threatened, waving the gun in the man's face.

"*Por favor, no señor*, I've done nothing to you," the farmer pleaded.

Without warning, Jack swung the barrel of the gun at the man's face, hitting him squarely on the temple. The man went down hard.

"Jack, what the hell are you doing?" Winslow shouted.

"Stay outta this! All these goddamed Mesicans got it coming."

Disoriented and not realizing that he should best stay down, the farmer moaned and started to get up.

"You keep your ass down there where you belong!" Jack yelled, as he hit the man again on the top of the head, this time knocking him unconscious.

"Let's get outta here!" Winslow yelled. "You're going to get us thrown in jail!"

Winslow grabbed Jack's arm, pulling him away from the old farmer who lay there bleeding and unconscious.

Jack was still yelling at the top of his lungs. "All them thievin' Mesicans oughta be shot!"

With all of the commotion, faces started poking out from behind window curtains and doors. Finally, when the Coffmans were far enough down the road, a caring soul came out to aid the farmer.

Robert Cartledge, the general manager of the Chisos Mining Company and now also the Justice of the Peace, learned of the incident the following morning. He called the Coffman brothers in to talk about what had happened.

"I hear you boys pistol whipped a Mexican last night," he said.

"Yeah, well, he called us some names, and I had to defend our honor," Jack said.

"Is that what happened?" Cartledge asked Winslow.

"It's whatever Jack said happened," he answered.

"You know guns aren't allowed in town," Cartledge said.

"Mr. Townsend gave us permission to carry them, since we're a guard and all that," Jack said.

"Well, carryin' a gun doesn't give you boys the right to go around beatin' up Mexicans," Cartledge said.

"No, sir," Winslow answered.

"Next time this happens, I'm throwing both your asses in jail. Do we understand each other?"

"Yes, sir," the Coffmans answered in unison.

The brothers walked out of Cartledge's office with nothing more than a slap on the hand.

11

Death Threat

Jorge unlocked and opened the front door of the store to let out the musty air that had accumulated overnight. He stepped out to sweep the wooden walkway when he noticed an envelope with his name scribbled on the front. He opened it to find an almost illegible note signed by Jack Coffman. As near as Jorge could make out, the note read:

> George,
>
> *You and your whole family are cheating sonsofabitches. You stole that truck from me. Next time I see any of you thieving Mexicans, I'm going to kill you. – J. Coffman*

It had been nearly two weeks since the card game. At first Jorge thought to take the note to Robert Cartledge. The kid was obviously still brooding about the incident. That wouldn't do much good, he thought. Cartledge would probably just throw the note in the wastebasket and tell him to watch his back. He figured that if the kid had wanted to do something, he'd have done it by now. Coffman had to know that if he followed through on his threat, he'd have hell cast upon him by the Villalbas. He didn't see fit to alarm anyone and kept the note to himself.

The Coffman boys still hadn't thought of a way of telling their father that they'd lost the truck and the typewriter that was in it to George Villalba. It was Winslow who came up with the idea of telling their father that Jorge bought the truck and the typewriter from them.

"Pa will go for that. He told us if we ever needed money, to sell the truck, right?"

"Yeah, but what'll we tell Pa we needed the money for?" Jack asked.

"Tell him we needed to buy us some rifles for the huntin' season. He'll buy that,"

"We'll tell him he signed a note for it and the typewriter," Jack added.

"We can show 'im a piece of paper with George's name on it. Hell, he ain't goin' to know any different."

They manufactured a note and signed it, "George Villalba." Jorge Villalba never used the name "George" in his life. Only Anglos called him that.

Their lack of skill at cards became well known. Gambling losses became a weekly event. Though they never played the Villalbas again, their deceit became so elaborate that at one point they went so far as to claim that Jorge asked for a loan on behalf of his father. Their ruse was as outrageous as it was comical.

No one other than their father knew of their supposed benevolence. He believed everything they told him, never bothering to verify any of the boys' assertions. On March 25, 1923, Coffman sent a letter to his boys. It read in part:

"*Sure busy* [on the farm], *need one of you boys awfully bad to help me...I hope Winslow is on the road, am looking for him every day. Have had some land cleared. Am going to plant corn next week—Let me hear from you."*

In another letter, he urged his sons to terminate their business relationship with Federico and Jorge Villalba. He wrote:

"Tell Geo. Villalba to pay for that truck or turn it back. And also, get the typewriter from George V… Tell old Fred Villalba to get busy and pay his acc[t], and get after old Sam Nail."

Mano a Mano

Saturday nights in Terlingua and Study Butte were usually filled with Mexican *bailes,* dances held on the west side. The Coffman boys were especially fond of these soirées. Liquid courage, their disdain for Mexicans and their disrespectful ways were always a surefire recipe for trouble.

On one fateful Saturday night, Winslow's mouth got him into a fight with a man who pulled a knife. The man stabbed Winslow just below the left shoulder blade. Some good Samaritans took Winslow to Carmen Castañeda, whose home was nearest to the *cantina.* The incident was reported to Justice of the Peace Cartledge who called Dr. Wilson and hauled him to Carmen's house. When Coffman saw Cartledge and the doctor walk in, he let loose a stream of profanities that would have made the devil blush. When Dr. Wilson heard the torrent of expletives, he immediately turned around and exited the house.

"Let the ungrateful sonofabitch lie there and bleed to death!" said the doctor on his way back to the car.

Cartledge hurried after the doctor, begging him to attend to Coffman. As much as he shared the doctor's sentiment, his sense of duty exceeded the contempt he felt for the young man. Dr. Wilson disinfected the wound with what was left of Winslow's sotol, finding a bit of pleasure in seeing him squirm as he poured. He stitched the young man up and quickly left.

"That little rogue and I were both lucky you were here," Wilson said to Cartledge as they drove away. "I was close to putting my Hippocratic Oath in my back pocket. He'd have died because of it, and I would have had to live with my sin. I'm not sure which fate would have been worse."

Two weeks later, Winslow sent Cartledge a letter:

Study Butte, Texas, Jan. 22, 1923

Mr. R. L. Cartledge,

Dear Mr. Carledge. About this trouble, I wish you would keep this quite [sic] and not say anything to my father. It would be trouble sure enough. I am going to stay away from those dances. Am not going to any more of them.

W. O. Coffman

P.S. Getting along fine.

Cartledge honored Winslow's request and never told Dan Coffman what happened. It most likely wouldn't have come as any surprise to the elder Coffman. He knew his boys had a taste for liquor and trouble.

Ed Gleim knew early on that he'd made a big mistake in hiring the Coffman boys. A year of imposing the insufferable brothers on the people of Study Butte was long enough. In March, while in Dallas on business, he wrote to his friend and partner, Federico, asking, almost pleading with him, to reconsider his proposal to merge their stores. Federico wrote back advising Gleim that he would consider joining forces with them, but only if it was his store that remained operational. Plans were put into play and arrangements were made to meet with Dan Coffman in Fort Davis to let him know that the Texas Almaden store would be closed and his boys' services would no longer be required.

Upon finding out about the meeting and fearing that his boys were on their way out, Dan Coffman, the boy's father, wrote the following letter:

> Jack, old E. M. G. [Ed Gleim] ran over this morning. Says G. W. Gleim wanted me to go over to Ft. Davis. He wanted to see me…I sure believe they are going to take that store or do something. Some one [sic] is telling or writing us up. I guess. So we had better get all we can up here [Shafter], in the land line. Reasons for me trading for this place. Let them have the job if they want it. We can make more here, my way.…Yes, Jack, I raised $300.00 in Alpine on the cows, for six months time. Am having a Devil of a time getting by, at present. Has old George Villalba paid for that truck or not? He was to pay the 15th this month. No mor [sic] news. I sent your ck to Marfa State Bank. Love, Dad.

By whatever means, Dan had learned that the Gleims and Federico were swapping correspondence. He'd heard a rumor sometime back that the two had talked about combining the stores. Gleim denied the gossip not wanting to spook his old friend. Dan had a hunch that Gleim was lying to him. He, however, mistakenly believed that Federico and Jorge were the moving parties in the scheme. He wrote to his sons:

> *Also found out something else on the road to Alpine. Old Geo. Villalba has been writing Gleimes [sic] about something and there is no telling what it is. He wants that job down there, of course. Now the thing is, watch them. Make old George pay for that truck by the 15th. I think it is $60.00 he owes. It is entered on the back of the note. If he don't pay, take the truck. I saw Bob C [Cartledge] on road. You see him and he will help you out. And when you get even [presumably with the Villalbas] let them go. I made the loan, all right. Got $300.00 from Alpine State Bank. I hope that old woman leaves there, if you need any help get old Simmons. And keep every thing locked up good....Getting late.*

> *Love, Dad.*

Dan never went to meet with the Gleim brothers. On May 23, 1923, Ed Gleim drove to Study Butte and terminated Jack and Winslow Coffman. He instructed the boys to surrender the keys to the store and the mine to Jorge Villalba. Needless to say, the young men were angry. They went directly to Robert Cartledge to complain about what had taken place.

The Justice of the Peace knew he was dealing with two irrational young men who kept threatening to have a showdown with Jorge.

Cartledge suggested they leave the keys with him, cool down and head back home to Shafter. He'd see to it that Jorge got the keys.

"The old Buick's got a bad leaf spring. Won't make it past the city limits, much less to Shafter," Jack said.

"Well, if you two boys keep talking about going after George, I'm going to have to put you both in protective custody until you cool off," Cartledge warned.

Winslow spoke up. "You don't have to do that, we'll be okay." The last thing he wanted to do was spend any time in jail, protective custody or no protective custody.

Jack looked over at his brother and nodded in agreement.

"Look, go on ahead to the company garage and tell old Leo to fix your car. I'll pay for it. You two head on outta here as soon as the car's repaired," Cartledge ordered.

Jack had lied. The car didn't run great, but it would have made it to Shafter just fine. The boys didn't want to leave for home just yet. They had some unfinished business to attend to.

The brothers headed to Terlingua to pick up two prostitutes, a blind musician named Florentino and a fresh bottle of sotol. Jack liked having Florentino and his guitar around whenever he drank.

"You sing mighty purdy fer a Mesican," Jack would tell the man. The boys drove to Study Butte for a going-away drunk before heading to Shafter. The four drank and partied through the night. Florentino slipped away unnoticed as the four passed out. When the brothers awoke, they popped open another bottle of sotol and continued their drinking where they'd left off.

"You know we gotta teach that George Villalba a lesson," Jack declared, after taking a swig of the sotol. "Ain't no Mesican got any right to take a job away from an American."

"Damn right!" Winslow said.

"Let's find that sonofabitch and tell him a thing or two," Jack said.

The boys and the girls piled into the car and went looking for Jorge. Their first stop was the Villalba bunkhouse next to the corrals used by *vaqueros* whenever cattle or horses were brought into town for sale.

No one was there. They made a mess of the place knocking over beds and strewing personal belongings everywhere. Upset that Jorge wasn't there, Jack took out his gun and shot up the place. He reloaded and drove over to the Villalba store. It was *siesta* time; the store was closed. They drove around to the front of the old Villalba house located a few hundred feet from the store.

It was the little house Federico had built for his family before they moved to the ranch. As caretaker of the store, Jorge lived in the house with his family. After lunch, Jorge had gone out to the veranda to take a mid-day *siesta*. Jacobo had come over earlier in the day with a string of horses he'd brought into town for sale.

Jacobo by Study Butte corral in happier times

He was inside visiting with Golla and the children when he heard yelling from the front of the house. He ran to the window as the Coffman brothers were walking up the dirt walkway with guns drawn.

"George, you are one thievin' sonofabitch. First you go stealing my truck now you go stealing our jobs. I oughta kill you just like I said!" he heard Jack Coffman yell before firing his first salvo of bullets.

Jorge's child, María, who had been napping with her father, innocently walked behind her father as bullets began whizzing by.

Jorge had braced for the pain of a bullet tearing through his flesh. He felt nothing. Jorge saw that the Coffmans were drunk. He figured that's why Jack had missed.

"You two just get back into your car and get out of here!" he yelled as he backed up, shielding his daughter with his body.

"We ain't goin' nowhere until we teach you a lesson!"

This time it was Winslow yelling as they both fired their weapons. Inside, Jacobo ran to Jorge's gunbelt hanging on the coat rack on the inside of the door. He grabbed the pistols and quickly fired off one shot from each gun through the open window.

Jorge saw the Coffmans fall to the ground and turned to see Jacobo standing at the window with guns drawn, smoke wafting from both barrels. Jacobo ran out and the two of them walked over to the wounded Coffmans. With baby Elia in her arms and Ruben at her side, Golla ran out and grabbed María, who was crying hysterically.

Jorge turned one, then the other brother over. Both were hit in the middle of the chest. Both had hit the ground dead.

"What are we going to do?" Jorge asked.

Little María Villalba and Ruben in front of their home in Study Butte

"They shot first," Jacobo said, defending his action.

"That isn't going to matter much. These are two Anglos. Who's going to believe that it was self-defense?" Jorge said. "We've got to turn ourselves in. Let's get Golla and the children over to Cartledge's place."

"What about Papá?" Jacobo asked.

"We'll send word to him. Barras is the first place they're going to look for us when they find out we're not in jail," Jorge said.

The Villalbas piled into the Coffman's Buick and drove the six miles to Terlingua and to the Justice of the Peace.

Cartledge opened the door to a frantic pounding. He was surprised to see Jorge Villalba.

"What in the Sam Hill is all the excitement about?"

"I shot and killed the Coffmans," Jorge said. "It was self-defense."

"You what?" Cartledge yelled.

"I'll tell you everything that happened, just let me get my family out of the car," Jorge pleaded.

"Sure, sure, bring 'em in," Cartledge said, still trying to digest what Jorge had told him.

Jorge waved for Jacobo and the others to come into the house. Once inside, he finished his account of what had happened. Jorge Villalba made the decision to shoulder the blame for the shootings. He didn't think it was much of a stretch since it was his guns that Jacobo used to shoot the Coffmans. He also thought that his little brother's reputation for being a hothead might be a detriment to their defense.

"Damn those boys!" Cartledge said. "They still at your place?" he asked.

"We were going to drag them into the house. Got as far as the porch, and thought better of it."

"We gotta get you and your family the hell outta Terlingua," Cartledge said. "When some of the townspeople find out what happened, they're going to want to lynch you two."

"Where are we going?" Jorge asked.

"I'm taking you to Alpine, to Everett Townsend's place," he told Jorge.

It was a harrowing trip to Alpine. Every approaching car was potentially someone gunning for the brothers. Cartledge allowed the Villalbas to keep their pistols and the .30-30 rifle Jorge had brought with him. They'd need extra firepower if they were to encounter any vigilantes.

At one point, Cartledge thought he saw Dan Coffman's car. He pulled over and frenetically ordered the Villalbas out of the car and behind a rock ledge that lined the road until the car passed. It wasn't Coffman.

They finally arrived in Alpine. Cartledge deposited the Villalbas, spoke briefly with Sheriff Townsend and quickly set out to return to Terlingua. He justifiably predicted an onslaught of activity within the Anglo community. To prevent the angry talk from escalating to a racial war, he needed to take measures to prevent some Anglos from retaliating against Mexican citizenry. All some Anglos needed was an excuse and this was probably the best one they'd ever had. Having made this point with Sheriff Townsend, plans were made to immediately send deputies to Terlingua to back up Cartledge.

Townsend knew that the 80 miles of road to Terlingua would soon be crawling with people looking for Jorge and Jacobo. Once they figured out that the Villalbas had been spirited out of Study Butte, the county jail would be the next place they would look. The sheriff's house would be the second. Townsend hid the Villalbas in his basement until he arranged to get them out of town. It wasn't until Jacobo told him of his ranch in México that the sheriff formulated a plan to smuggle them across the Río Grande.

12

Fighting for the Family's Survival

Enjoying the evening air, Federico was sitting with Severita on the porch after dinner when they saw an unexpected visitor. Federico reached behind for the .270 Winchester rifle that leaned against the wall. A weapon was always nearby anytime he was outdoors. He knew the rider's face but not his name. The horse's nostrils flared and belly heaved, as foamy sweat oozed from beneath the saddle blanket. He'd been ridden hard. The rider's legs trembled as he dismounted and stood doubled over trying to take in enough breath to talk. Just as Federico was about to ask the young man his purpose, the messenger spoke words that would tear his world apart.

"There was a gunfight. Jorge and Jacobo shot and killed Jack and Winslow Coffman," the boy said between long breaths.

"Are my boys okay?" Federico said, shocked at what he'd heard.

"Yes."

"What happened?"

"I don't know exactly. All I know is that the brothers showed up at your son's house, and they got shot. I don't know any more than that."

"Where are they now?" Federico asked.

"Jorge said Cartledge was taking them, Golla and the children to Alpine."

Federico was certain his boys were being delivered to Everett Townsend. Federico thanked and dispatched the boy, and immediately instructed Severita to pack for a trip to Alpine. He sent word to Emilio to have some men come to stay at the compound in the event Anglos came to retaliate.

News of the Coffman brothers' deaths spread quickly. *The Alpine Avalanche* wrote the following article:

> *Immediately after the news of the killing was received, Dr. R. A. Wilson and Mr. T. M. Newton hurried to the scene with the hope that the boys or one of them might still be alive. They were both dead, shot through the breast and lying side by side, their pistols also by them. They were near the door on Billalba's [sic] porch as he said. Beyond this nothing is known of the fight or the cause, except there is a rumor that the affair came up over a reported change in management of the mining company business or store. One of the Coffman boys was in charge of the store which is near the Billalba's home.*

The bodies of the Coffman boys were taken to the Livingston Funeral Company in Alpine where they were displayed for viewing on the grounds of the funeral home. They were placed on a table under a shed. Many traveled from Study Butte and Terlingua to pay their respects. The brothers' transgressions and the contempt most people had for them seemed to be forgotten in death. People spoke of the two in front of Dan Coffman and his wife as if their sons had been innocent, respectful young men.

The *Alpine Avalanche Supplemental* published an obituary:

> *Like all children they were the apple of their parents' eyes…At one fell sweep all that they hold dear is gone. They had hopes and aspirations for their boys like all parents…[They] took them to San Antonio where they were given a business course. But some way, the Providence that rules the lives of men has decided otherwise and the boys have finished their race here on earth…Although men in stature and size, they were but boys, Winslow being 21 and Jack, 19, almost twenty. They were boys that feared no danger and possibly therein lay their fate…It seems a pity, a pity that they should be cut off right in the bloom of life, but He who rules the destinies of men knows why these things must be. Help us to understand.*

By Thursday, Sheriff Townsend had arranged for the Villalbas to return to Alpine and surrender. Deputy T. I. Morgan took them into custody at Rancho Barras.

Jorge was charged with murder and Jacobo with complicity. When questioned, Jorge denied that his brother was at his house when the shooting occurred. He told Cartledge that Jacobo was busy driving a herd of horses from the ranch. He was nearing the corrals, not far from the house, when he heard the gunshots and hurried over. He claimed that by the time Jacobo got to the house he had shot both Coffmans.

W. D. Smithers, a long-time resident of Terlingua, would later tell Cartledge that he saw Jacobo Villalba at the store and later at Jorge's home that day long before the shootings. Smithers insisted that the horses had been corralled since mid-morning.

Federico's first opportunity to talk to his sons came two days later after their arrival in Santa Elena.

"Papá, how did you find us?" Jacobo asked as he greeted the horse and buggy that also carried Severita and Lico.

"I told Townsend to bring you here," Federico said.

Federico helped Severita from the buggy as Lico stepped out from the opposite side. Lico gave Jorge a big hug, crying as he made his way to Golla and the children. He always wore his emotions on his sleeve.

"You knew about my place?" Jacobo asked in surprise.

"*Mi hijo*, I know everything that happens on both sides of the border."

"Who told you?" Jacobo asked, thinking it might have been one of the Baizas.

"Don Santiago came to the ranch to ask permission to sell you *Los Fuegos*," Federico said, drawing an even bigger look of surprise from his son. Federico walked into the house with familiarity and fondness. He'd enjoyed Don Santiago's hospitality many times.

"Then you must also know how I bought it."

"I've known all along," Federico said.

"Why haven't you said anything?"

"I raised my children to make their own decisions. You in particular have not always made the best ones, but you've always been man enough to abide by their consequences. I told you how I felt about this so-called 'venture' but you decided to undertake it, nevertheless. At a point where I would have seen you acting irresponsibly or endangering yourself or the family, I would have stepped in and put a stop to it. Unfortunately, the same can't be said for Dan Coffman. Now tell me. What happened?"

Federico pulled out a chair for his wife and another for himself as he settled in at the kitchen table.

Jorge spoke first.

"They were upset that Mr. Gleim had fired them. They came to the house to kill me. They were drunk. I tried to talk them into leaving; instead they pulled their guns and started shooting. María was in back of me. I backed towards the house shielding María with my body when I heard two shots from inside the house."

"It was me," Jacobo interrupted. "I shot them. If I hadn't they would have killed Jorge and little María. I had no choice, Papá."

"I believe you, son." Federico said, reaching across and squeezing his son's hand. Federico looked at Jorge.

"Word around town has it that you killed the brothers."

"That's what I told Cartledge. I figured that if I told the truth, it would go harder on Jacobo because of his reputation."

"I raised you to always tell the truth; this is one time you were right not to," Federico said, thoroughly shaken at what he had just heard. "I'm bringing an attorney from Mead & Metcalfe to meet with you on Wednesday."

"Isn't that the law firm that's handling the Chisos land deal?" Jorge asked.

"One and the same," Federico answered.

"What's all of this going to cost, Papá?" Jacobo asked.

"You just concern yourself with telling the man everything that happened. You let me worry about the cost."

Santos was whisked away to Fort Davis the Monday after the shooting. Uncle Max had been summoned for the expressed purpose of getting the Villalba women and Santos out of harm's way. As it turned out, the women refused to go.

Regina ordered one of the *vaqueros* to ride to Ciudad Acuña to tell Miguel what had happened. She gave the man a note that asked Miguel to come as soon as possible.

Legal Wrangling

Attorney Charles E. Mead and a court stenographer arrived at Rancho Barras Tuesday afternoon. They were greeted by armed *vaqueros* and a weary Federico and Severita.

"Doesn't look like you've gotten much sleep," Mead said to Federico as they climbed the stairs.

"These are trying times," Federico said. "Are you folk hungry?"

Mead cleared the dust out his throat. "Hungry and thirsty!" he said.

Little of substance was discussed during dinner. Federico offered his study for the meeting Mead requested before settling in for the night.

"Do you mind if I light up my pipe?" Federico asked his guest.

Mead chuckled. "I was about to ask you if I could smoke my cigar."

Both lit their smokes and settled back into the overstuffed armchairs.

"Brandy?" Federico asked.

"Lovely," Mead answered.

Federico poured himself and Mead a snifter of *Cardenal Mendoza* brandy that he drank only with company.

"Mr. Villalba, I'm not going to lie to you. This is going to be an uphill battle," Mead said as he took a sip of the brandy. "My God, this is wonderful!" he exclaimed as he held the glass up to the rays of sunlight that shone through the window facing them. "I'm not going to drink all of this so I can soak some of my cigars in this amber ambrosia."

Federico smiled. "Drink as much as you want. I have plenty of brandy and a container for soaking cigars. You're welcome to both," he offered.

"You are too kind." With that, Mead's face turned serious again. "There are a lot of people out there who would like to see your boys hang."

"How hard could it be to prove self-defense?"

"If it was the other way around and your boys were Anglo and the deceased were Mexican…not too hard," Mead said with a shrug of the shoulders. "One of the problems we face is that we have no witnesses. Another is that I'm not sure your boys are telling the truth."

"What makes you think they aren't telling the truth?" Federico asked.

"Mr. Villalba, I am having a hard time believing that Jorge could have had time to back up into the house, retrieve his guns and get two shots off, all while the Coffman boys were coming towards him with blazing guns." Mead paused to take a long sip of his drink. He licked his lips then resumed speaking. "This is wonderful brandy. You'll have to tell me where I might get some."

"It's imported from Spain. I have an extra bottle you can have."

"I'll be happy to buy it from you," Mead insisted.

"It would please me if you would accept it as a gift." There was a tinge of frustration in Federico's voice as the attorney wasted time fussing over the liquor.

Federico let the man talk. He was curious to know what conclusions he might have reached.

"As I was saying, there is no way Jorge could have shot the two unless he'd already had the pistols in hand when the Coffmans showed up. Besides, I went to inspect the bodies. My gut tells me that Jacobo was somehow involved in the shooting."

"Jorge said he shot them. That's how it will stay."

"That's fine—what I have to do is keep the emphasis off of who shot whom and call attention to why. The Coffman boys were bad seeds, there's no denying that. They were most definitely shooting at Jorge. Hell, there are enough bullet holes in the house to prove that," Mead said with an animated nod of the head.

"You've been to the house?" Federico asked.

"Stopped there before we came here," he said. "It doesn't appear the Coffmans were shot on the porch."

Federico listened intently, impressed with Mead's knowledge of the shooting. "How is it you know that?" Federico asked, looking squarely in the attorney's eyes.

"It was barely visible because of all the trampling that'd been done by curiosity seekers, but I could make out a trail of blood from about the middle of the dirt walkway to the porch as well as some drag marks."

"Do you think the sheriff's come to these same conclusions?" Federico asked.

"I talked to the sheriff. He's pretty much relying on Terlingua's Justice of the Peace for details of the incident.

I don't think I'm going to have much trouble discrediting his investigative efforts, should the prosecutor choose to give them any weight."

"It sounds as if you have the situation well in hand," Federico said. "How much is all of this going to cost me?"

"I've devoted my entire staff to your case, including an investigator. As near as I can figure, our fee is going to be about $25,000.

Amazed at the number Mead had just thrown at him, Federico responded with concern in his voice. "I don't have that kind of money."

"We can get started with a $3,000 retainer. Can you borrow the money or perhaps sell some of your property to come up with the balance?" the attorney asked.

Federico studied Mead's face for a bit before answering. "Maybe...I don't know. Can you give me some time to come up with the money?"

"Let me talk to my partner," Mead said, leaning forward in his chair to give Federico a reassuring glance. "We'll work something out."

As it turned out, Federico sold his leather goods business in Santa Elena to come up with the money for the retainer.

Federico and Mead left for Santa Elena early the following morning. Severita, Regina and Lico stayed behind. As the buggy left the compound, Emilio rode up to Villalba to tell him that intruders had been chased off the night before.

"How many?" Federico asked.

"Judging by the hoof prints, four men. They hightailed it as soon as they knew we were on to them," Emilio told his *patrón*.

"Double the watch," Federico ordered his foreman. "I'll be back by dinner time."

"*¡Vayan con Dios*," Emilio shouted, as the buggy jerked forward.

"Looks like you've got a good man," Mead commented.

"He is. I trust him with my family's life," Federico said, snapping the reins a second time to quicken the horse's pace. "Do you know how to use a gun?"

"Quite well, thank you. I've got one in my waist band under my coat," Mead said.

"Good, you might need it."

Thankfully, the trip was uneventful both ways. Mead spent almost six hours taking statements from the brothers. The men returned to a dinner of stewed rabbit, one of Federico's favorite meals. From the small portion Mead ate, it was apparent he didn't share Villalba's palate for the delicacy. He ate more biscuits and *frijoles* than meat. After dinner the men retired to Federico's study, this time to drink, not to talk.

Miguel Returns to Rancho Barras

Miguel accompanied the courier that delivered Regina's letter back to the ranch where a somber and surprised Villalba family greeted him. Regina had said nothing about having sent for him, not even to Severita.

"Thank you for coming," Regina said as she walked toward Miguel who stood in the doorway waiting to be invited in. She reached for Miguel's hand and pulled him to the center of the great room where the family had retreated after dinner. Severita stood up and came to Miguel with an exuberant hug. Federico remained in his chair.

"I am sorry to have returned under such terrible circumstances," Miguel responded, pausing for a moment to look at Don Federico for a reaction.

The old man had mixed feelings about Miguel's return. He was perturbed by his daughter's affectionate manner towards the schoolteacher. It became all too apparent that they had kept in contact even after his admonitions. He would confront the issue. Now was not the time.

"Are you ready to work teacher?" Federico asked.

"Wherever you need me," Miguel said.

"Are you hungry?" Regina asked, ignoring her father's brashness.

Miguel nodded yes. Regina and Miguel walked to the kitchen where she could feed him and properly greet him, minus an audience.

"Where is Lico?" Miguel asked as he sat in front of the plate Regina had prepared for him.

"He's with Jorge and Jacobo at the ranch in Santa Elena," she said.

"This is quite a mess, isn't it?"

"It has turned our lives upside down," Regina said.

"I saw many men guarding the ranch. It appears your entire family is in great danger. Why don't you and Severita stay in Santa Elena?"

"Golla is there to tend to my brothers. I am needed here, not in México."

Miguel studied Regina's face as he sipped his coffee. "Your father is angry that I have returned."

"I suppose he is."

Regina took a deep breath and looked down at the lace trimmed handkerchief whose corners she'd been pinching and tugging at.

"He has not forgiven me for having ended my relationship with Francisco."

"I think we should get married," Miguel said.

Regina looked up at Miguel with a most incredulous look on her face.

"¿Estás loco?" she said, hunching over the table and lowering her voice so no one in the next room could hear her.

"What makes you think I would marry you?" she asked, half-whispering.

"With all that's happening I should be the one to protect you. I would be less than a man if I wasn't willing to stand between you and danger."

"That's a noble gesture, but I am perfectly capable of taking care of myself."

"I'm not saying you're not. I love you, and would give my life for you. I want to watch over you day and night. Allow me that privilege by becoming my wife."

"Even if I wanted to marry you, this would have to be the worst possible time for us to bring up the subject. I know my father would not give you my hand in marriage."

"There is never going to be a good time for your father." Miguel took another sip of his coffee before continuing. "I've given it great thought, and whether or not your father agrees, I think we should get married, and soon."

Miguel's eyes had an intensity Regina had never seen before. She fell back in her chair. In Miguel's absence she had felt helpless and hopeless. Miguel brought happiness and a feeling of security.

"We'll talk to my father, but at a time of my choosing. Understood?"

Miguel smiled. "Understood."

Cartledge and
Sheriff Townsend

Robert Cartledge had never seen the likes of all that was going on in the Big Bend as a result of the shootings. Anglos had been shot and killed before. Those killings never stirred up the emotions that the Coffman brothers' demise had. One of the first things the Justice of the Peace did was hold a town meeting. He wasn't sure whether that did more harm than good. One of the more militant of the townspeople kept shouting that the Villalbas ought to be gunned down the same as they gunned down the Coffman boys. It did little good to explain to them that it appeared to have been self-defense. Cartledge made few allies that evening. He finally had to threaten the group with incarceration for any man or woman who incited violence against the Villalbas or any Mexican.

The Coffmans were taken to Marathon for burial. If the Coffmans had been any older, it's doubtful their deaths would have elicited much sympathy. It's also doubtful that they would have lived much longer than they did. Bullets with their names on them were in many gun chambers throughout Terlingua and Study Butte. It so happened the Coffmans chose one of the Villalbas to pull the trigger. Justice of the Peace Cartledge played a minor, almost non-existent role in the investigation into the Coffman killings. His involvement in the matter pretty much ended when he delivered the Villalbas to the sheriff.

Sheriff Townsend, like everyone else, knew that Terlingua justice was dispensed in the shadow of the Chisos Mining Company.

"*El Bob*," as the Mexican citizenry called Cartledge, and his boss Howard Perry had no interest in working to help exonerate any

Mexican who had killed an Anglo—especially when the Mexican was a Villalba.

Cartledge's cooperation with the defense firm consisted of his commitment to testify about his run-ins with the boys and what he found and saw at the scene of the killings. He made it clear that he would not characterize the Villalbas in any better light than the circumstance would dictate. "I ain't about to gild any goddamed lily," he told defense attorney Mead.

Sheriff Townsend interviewed anyone and everyone who had any contact with the Coffman brothers. The more he dug, the clearer it became that the brothers had chosen their day to die.

"It was the darndest case of suicide two boys ever committed," the sheriff told District Attorney Brian "Monty" Montague.

"You won't convince Dan Coffman of that," Montague said. "He swears up and down that if his boys had intended on killing old George, they'd a done it. 'My boys never missed a shot in their lives…never missed a shot in their lives,' he kept repeating to me. He's convinced his boys were merely firing warning shots."

"Not likely," Townsend submitted. "There were eleven holes in George's house, all were chest high. They were aiming for George—just too drunk to hit anything. They were two dangerous men. Neither ever saw a 'bugger' in his life, til that day," Townsend said.

"Do you believe Jake killed the boys and not George?" Montague asked.

"Doesn't really matter does it?" Townsend said with a wry smile.

At torney Charles Mead

Shortly after being retained, Mead wondered why the case had been accepted for prosecution by the Brewster County District Attorney in the first place.

He was happy at the opportunity to make his fee. He almost felt guilty for demanding and receiving the prized Rancho Barras in payment for his fee to handle the defense. Mead knew the ranch was worth considerably more than $25,000, but he also knew the state of the economy would provide little chance for Federico to produce that much money through any partial sale of his property. But, his remorse was superficial and fleeting. The reality around these parts was that if a Mexican killed two white men, he was in serious trouble whatever the circumstance. Only the best and most expensive legal representation could save such an otherwise doomed soul.

But this was such a clear case of defense of self, home and family, Mead thought. Didn't much matter that the defendant was Mexican. Nor should it matter that the deceased were white and shot through the heart. The sonsofabitches deserved it. Had they pulled a stunt like this at anyone else's place, no such charges would ever have been brought.

At first, Mead reckoned that the whole prosecution would be based on ethnicity. It wouldn't do for Mexicans to think that they could kill a white man with impunity. After months of investigation, however, he began to see the reality of the case. It was a prosecution based upon political considerations and favor.

It was well known that Howard Perry and the Villalbas had a long-standing dislike for each other. They were more than competitors.

Fred Villalba was an affront to Perry's otherwise unquestioned authority in Terlingua. Perry wasn't toothless. He was a master political strategist. He understood the workings of political strength and was cunning and effective in its acquisition and use. After all, this was someone who had enough political clout to arrange for the United States government to send a military detachment to an outpost like Lajitas, Texas.

Recruiting the local D.A. in a tiny rural community must have been small potatoes for Perry. Mead recognized political favor when he saw it. The reality was that regardless of the outcome of this trial, at its conclusion, Fred Villalba would no longer be the high and mighty "Mexican" around these parts. No longer would the Villalba clan be a thorn in the side of Howard Perry's businesses or political machinery.

One other aspect of the prosecution had puzzled Mead from the beginning. Why charge Jorge and Jacobo with the murder of only Winslow Coffman, the older of the brothers? Why not charge him for the murders of both?

Jack Coffman, the younger brother, had quite a reputation and history for violence. Winslow, on the other hand, was older, cleaner, and therefore more presentable as a hapless victim. Montague had to have figured that his case would be easier if he limited the prosecution to the murder of Winslow. In this manner, he'd be able to somehow minimize mention or reference to the younger Jack's extensive history of violence, while focusing the jury on the more sympathetic Winslow. Mead wasn't going to let Montague sanitize the facts by re-posturing the case. He aimed to hold his feet to the fire. He would embarrass him before the jury for playing fast and loose with such a serious matter. The younger brother Jack's background was fair game and was going to be admissible.

At this realization, Mead leaned back in his chair. His grin grew to a wide smile. Mead was flush with the confidence of a high-rolling gambler in the company of lady luck. He had himself a winner.

13

A Troubled Family

Jacobo grew more impatient by the day. He had shot and killed two men. Two months after the shootings, at Federico's insistence, he'd stepped back from his bootlegging business, allowing Valentín and his family to take over the operation.

As expected, Candelario assumed the leadership role. It didn't sit well with Jacobo, but there was nothing he could do about it. His father had given strict orders to disassociate himself from the illicit operation and the Baizas. He did as he was told except for continuing to maintain contact with Valentín. His friend would sneak across the border and keep him apprised of everything that was happening on the other side of the Río Grande. The rumor mill was teeming with wild stories ranging from him and Jorge running off to central México to avoid prosecution to having been killed by Dan Coffman's hired guns.

The Villalba brothers busied themselves with working the ranch and building up their herd of cattle. Federico sent his boys ten stud bulls that he'd bought at auction. They would join the other eight he already had to service his five hundred or so Herefords. Jacobo also kept himself occupied with Carmelita, his new girlfriend.

Jorge, on the other hand, had his family to care for. Golla was pregnant with their fourth child. She was beside herself, worrying about her husband. Her heart ached at the thought that he might be in prison during the birth of their baby?

Back at Rancho Barras, Regina had decided it was time for her and Miguel to speak to her father about getting married. She went to her father's study to let Miguel know that they would break the news to Federico that night.

"I fear no man, but I must tell you that I am truly apprehensive of your father's reaction when we tell him," Miguel said.

"He's not going to shoot you," Regina said, trying to add some levity.

"You never know. He might want to add a trophy to the others on his wall," Miguel said with a nervous smile.

Regina smiled and moved to the chair next to her father's desk and plopped herself in it.

"He must know its coming. Papá is no dummy. I've certainly dropped enough hints about my wanting to leave the ranch."

"That may soften the blow," said Miguel. "It's not going to take away the sting of his daughter not marrying a blue blood. I know that's what he wanted for you and anything less is unacceptable."

"Are you going to ask for my hand in marriage or not?"

"Of course I am!" Miguel said, amused at Regina's eagerness. "I am merely thinking out loud. Before dinner or after dinner?"

"After dinner. I don't want to ruin Papá's meal."

"I'm willing to bet we would ruin a lot more than his dinner," Miguel said.

Severita's heart was heavy. Federico was a complex man of unquestionable strength and character. But in their private moments, it was different. She could see him unraveling, and she was worried.

"We will get through this," she assured her husband as she cut potatoes for the dinner meal.

Deep in thought, Federico sipped his brandy at the kitchen table. Staring ahead, he pondered what his wife had just said. It was frightening how helpless he now felt.

Federico drank the last of his brandy, scooted his chair out from the table and stood up.

"I've got to see to that heifer that's about to birth," he said. Tell Regina to come out to the barn. I might need her help."

"Federico!" Severita said, as he reached the door that led to the courtyard.

Her husband stopped dead in his tracks without turning to look back at her. "What do you want?" he asked.

"Don't shut me out."

Federico hesitated a moment before responding, angry at himself for having played down his wife's feelings.

"I'm sorry," he said, turning and offering his wife a meek smile as a peace offering.

"I have got so much on my mind," he said.

"You're not facing this alone you know," Severita reminded him.

"I know," he replied. "I know."

Federico had just pulled the cow from the corral into the barn when Regina arrived.

"She's in labor!" he shouted.

Federico slid his arm into the Hereford to count hooves. She looked big enough to have more than one calf inside.

"Only one, but feels like it's in breach. Get me that chain that's hanging on the wall," he ordered.

Regina scurried over and retrieved the chain. Federico deftly looped the chain around the front hoof and started pulling.

"Give me a hand, *hija*," They both pulled. Slowly, little hooves appeared. A few more heaves and a slippery calf fell to the straw. Regina immediately reached down and started removing the mucous from the calf's nose.

"It's a girl," she said. Federico was attending to the cow who wanted up now that she'd taken care of business.

"Good," he said over his shoulder. "We can always use more heifers."

Regina reached for the burlap sack her father had brought into the stall and gently wiped the afterbirth off the calf.

The baby was warm and soft. Regina reached under the calf and brought it to its legs. She held on as the calf rocked back and forth until it was able to stand on its own. The wobbly white face immediately went to her mom to do what came natural to all babies, animal or human.

Regina and Miguel Confront Federico

Regina and Miguel barely touched their plates at dinner, something that did not go unnoticed by Severita. She followed Regina to the kitchen after they picked up the men's plates. "What's up with you two?" Severita asked.

"Miguel's going to ask for my hand in marriage tonight."

"Do you think now is the right time?" Severita asked, thoroughly confused by Regina's timing.

"There will never be a 'right time'," Regina said.

Severita thought for a second before she replied. "Can't it wait until after the trial?"

"What then? What will make my father more agreeable to my plans...tell me? His concerns are his boys, his ranch and you. Where do I fit in?" she asked. "He wanted me to marry Francisco so he could expand his kingdom. You said it yourself. Why can't I do something to make me happy?"

Severita paused before she answered. "Why don't you wait a day or two?" She suggested. She knew that in Federico's fragile state of mind, today was not the day.

"It's going to be tonight!" Regina declared, not leaving room for further argument.

Federico retired to the porch to smoke his pipe. He'd barely lit it when Regina and Miguel walked out.

"Papá, we need to talk to you," Regina said.

"The two of you?" Federico asked with a curious look on his face.

"Don Federico, I am here to ask for your daughter's hand in marriage," Miguel said.

Federico's face reddened with anger.

"You may not have it," he responded firmly. "Regina, what is the meaning of this? You must have known I would never agree to let you marry Miguel. What does he have to offer you?"

"Happiness," she responded with little hesitation.

"You can't eat happiness," her father replied. "You could have married a man that offered wealth and security. Why would you choose a schoolteacher that has barely enough to take care of himself, much less a family? No. Absolutely not, you cannot marry this man!"

Miguel started to defend himself when he was abruptly interrupted by Regina.

"*Papá*, I will marry Miguel with or without your blessing," she said, scowling down at her father.

"You do, and I will disown you!" Federico shouted, eyes glaring angrily at his daughter.

"Then so be it. We will leave for Fort Davis tomorrow at daylight," Regina announced.

"Leave and you will never be welcomed in this house again," Federico said.

Regina bolted for the door, grabbing Miguel's hand and pulling him behind her.

"It can't end like this," Miguel said.

"Go pack your things," Regina commanded, ignoring Miguel's remarks. "We're leaving tonight. I will not spend another night in this house."

Within the hour, Miguel and Regina were on their way to Fort Davis in one of her father's trucks. Regina drove. They arrived at her Uncle Max's home at midnight. After an hour of explanation, all went to bed.

Regina and Miguel arranged to be married on July 19, 1923, at St. Josephs in Ft. Davis, the church where Federico married María. Word was sent to Federico of the impending wedding. None of the Villalbas attended the ceremony or the reception held in Terlingua.

Legal Maneuvers

The Grand Jury convened on July 25, 1923. Over the next few weeks it subpoenaed and heard testimony from all of the Villalbas and a substantial number of Terlingua and Study Butte's Anglo citizenry. Aside from Jorge and Jacobo's family, not one Mexican citizen was interviewed. The fact that the Coffmans dispensed their terrorism on the Mexican community almost exclusively was completely discounted.

On August 14, the Grand Jury officially dismissed the charges against Jacobo because his whereabouts at the time of the killings could not be pinpointed. Jorge was indicted for murder only in the death of Winslow Coffman. They must have figured Jack Coffman had it coming. In truth, using Jorge and Winslow as the front men in the case made things cleaner, simpler and easier.

District Attorney Montague's considerations were identical to those in the Villalba camp. Mead grinned at the irony of it all, deciding it would be a good tactical move to immediately file a motion for a trial date.

After a long conversation with Sheriff Townsend, Montague set up a meeting with Jorge Villalba's defense attorneys. The sheriff convinced the D.A. that going to trial right away would do more harm than good. Montague arranged to meet with defense counsel to discuss timing.

Montague arrived at the luxurious offices of Mead & Metcalfe at half-past ten. A matronly lady who introduced herself as Mr. Mead's legal secretary greeted him. Montague waited for nearly half an hour before Mead appeared in the waiting room.

"Monty, how the hell are ya'?" Mead said excitedly as he extended his hand to the district attorney.

"We're going to meet in the conference room if you don't mind."

As soon as he released the prosecutor's hand, Mead walked quickly out the door and down the hallway. Montague trailed behind taking two steps to every one of Mead's, who was a good six inches taller.

The conference room door was open. Montague entered to find Hunter Metcalfe and six of the firm's attorneys seated at the table. Montague hesitated, wondering where he should sit.

Metcalfe smiled. "Counselor, why don't you sit over here next to me?"

One of the staff got up and closed the door as Montague took his chair.

"If I'd known you were going to have half of your staff in on the meeting, I would have at least brought my assistant," Montague said.

"Don't let all these people intimidate you. You arrived at the tail end of a staff meeting. I asked them to stay because they're all involved in our client's defense, in one way or another. You don't mind, do you?" Metcalfe asked.

"That's fine," the prosecutor said, though he didn't really mean it.

"Okay," Mead said, "Where do we start?"

"I need a continuance," Montague said.

"Brian, this should never have gone to trial in the first place," Mead said. "It's as clear as day that it was self-defense."

"You know that and I know that, but who are we to challenge the infinite wisdom of the Grand Jury?" Montague asked.

"Answer me this. Why should we give you the opportunity to mount any kind of attack?"

"That's not why I'm asking. I met with Sheriff Townsend, he said I 'didn't have a crooked stick to lean on in this case.' He's right. If we try the case now and your client is set free, Townsend assures me that if Dan Coffman doesn't kill him, they're plenty of other people out there that will. Federico is a good friend of his. He asked me as a personal favor to move for a continuance to let tempers cool."

Metcalfe frowned. "That sounds like a mighty lame reason to me. I know the Villalbas. They can darn well take care of themselves."

"Look, all I want to do is the right thing," the D.A. said. "If we try the case now and your client's acquitted, all hell's going to break loose."

"Isn't this something? We've got the toughest prosecutor west of the Pecos in our office, and he's worried about a defendant. That's gotta be a first," Metcalfe said, marveling at the circumstance.

"And probably the last," Montague cautioned.

Metcalfe looked at his partner. "What do you think, Charles?"

"We don't need it, but we can probably take advantage of the additional time," Mead said, pausing. "I say we give it to him."

"We'll withdraw our motion and not oppose yours. Go ahead and ask for your continuance," Metcalfe proffered with an air of competence and self-assurance. "We all here know it's only delaying the inevitable."

The next day, Charles Mead gathered the staff, including his investigator, to discuss the firm's strategy. He'd tagged the trial as and easy one, but he wasn't about to put forth anything less than the firm's most aggressive defense. He wanted to make it clear to his team that absolutely nothing regarding the case would be treated lightly. Names of potential witness were assigned in groups. Three of his junior associates were assigned twenty-three names collectively.

His investigator, Nate Rogers, a former Texas Ranger, was to meet with Robert Cartledge and Everett Townsend. He knew them both from when he was a ranger. Mead didn't expect all twenty people to testify; he wanted no one or nothing to fall through the cracks. Names on the list included Jorge's wife, his father, brothers, as well as Severita. The others were townspeople they would call as character witnesses. Mead knew that several of the people on the list were of mutual interest to the prosecutor's office. Howard Perry was on neither list. Both attorneys agreed not to call any hostile witnesses.

Rogers and Raleigh Crawford, a bilingual first-year associate, were assigned to interview Florentino, the blind musician, and Benny the *cantinero*. They set out for Terlingua the next day.

"Where'd you learn to speak Spanish?" Rogers asked Crawford.

"Had a Mexican nanny," the young attorney answered.

To Rogers, the word nanny conjured up images that were foreign to these parts. Rich people, big city, big houses with parks full of nannies pushing baby carts. He looked at the young lawyer curiously.

"A nanny, huh!" the former ranger said. "I can speak the lingo too, but I didn't learn it from no nanny. I learned by living among them. I grew up in Marathon. Half my buddies were Mexican— still are."

"Why'd you leave the Rangers?" Crawford asked.

"Got so that most of them felt like they could do anything they wanted to anyone they wanted. Wasn't for me. The last straw was when a ranger for no good reason killed one of the Mexican friends I grew up with. He claimed Pedro drew on him. Pedro couldn't hit the broad side of a barn. He never would have drawn on anybody, much less a ranger. Anyway, the ranger got away with it. I got out."

"How about you, kid? What brings you all the way from New York? Chuck tells me you graduated from Princeton."

"Chuck?" the attorney asked.

"Okay, Charles."

"Oh, you mean Mr. Mead. I was recruited. His partner, Mr. Metcalfe, is a Princeton grad. He came up and talked to us. I liked what he said."

"Did you know where'd you be coming?"

"Not really, but I don't regret it. I don't plan on making my life here. I figured I'd give it two or three years, then go back and hook up with a big firm."

"What do you think about this case?" Rogers asked.

"I sure feel bad for the Coffman boys, but there's no question they were looking for trouble and found it in a big way."

They arrived in Boquillas around noon. Chata's was their first stop. The Chisos Mining Company in Terlingua was the second. The young attorney was introduced to Chata and her *chile verde.* After lunch, the two drove to Cartledge's office. From there Crawford left alone for Florentino's home armed with directions from the Justice of the Peace, while Rogers stayed to interview Cartledge.

Cartledge's office was a small room barely able to house him and a few file cabinets. A rickety fold-up wooden chair reserved for guests was retrieved from in back of the door. The only light in the room streamed in from grimy windows that overlooked the furnaces and condensing units at shaft No. 8, once Chisos' most prolific source of cinnabar.

"Good to see you, Nate. Have a seat." The two shook hands. Cartledge unfolded the chair and put it next to his desk.

Rogers stared at the chair that had seen better days, wondering if it would hold his 6-foot-2, 220-pound frame.

Cartledge must have seen the apprehension in his face. "Don't worry, it ain't gonna break."

Rogers, nonetheless, sat down gingerly until he was certain the chair wouldn't collapse under him.

Cartledge pulled a notebook from the middle drawer in his desk that presumably contained notes about the shootings.

"Hang on for a second," he said just as it looked like he was ready to start the interview. Cartledge got up, took two steps to a small fan on one of the file cabinets and switched it on. "Gettin' hot in here," he said as he sat down, leaning back in the chair. "What ya' got for me?"

"I'm not going to take too much of your time. Just need you to answer a few questions about the shooting."

With that, Rogers opened his notepad, ready to record Cartledge's statements.

"I understand the Coffman boys were on the porch when Dr. Wilson arrived at the house," Rogers said.

"Yeah, looked like that's where they got shot."

"He didn't mention seeing any blood midway up the walk?" Rogers asked.

"Nope, Doc never said a thing about that."

"How soon after you returned from Alpine, did you go to Study Butte?"

"Directly, didn't even go home."

"What'd you see?"

"Hell, by the time I got there everything had been trampled. I think half the city came to look at where the boys had been killed." Cartledge took a sip of cold coffee from a mug that looked like it had never been washed. "Can I get you something to drink?" he asked.

"No, that's fine, I just had lunch," Rogers said, repulsed at the sight of the mug. "Tell me, did you take any precautionary measures to prevent any one else from damaging or removing evidence?"

"I put a man at the house for the next couple of days, mostly to keep some of the more unruly townspeople from burning down the place."

"Okay, now tell me about any and all run-ins you had with the brothers. I understand the boys were pretty rowdy."

Cartledge proceeded to recite the Coffman's history while they lived in Terlingua, taking considerable time to pontificate about his positive involvement in their lives.

Couldn't have been too positive, Rogers thought. *Didn't keep them from getting killed.* "Sheriff Townsend tells me no witnesses came forth. Any come forward since?"

"Nope." Cartledge turned slowly and put his hand on his notebook.

"Something in there you need to look at?" Rogers asked.

Cartledge thought for a moment.

"No—not really," he said, changing his mind, then turning back to lock eyes with Rogers. "You might want to talk to W. D. Smithers. He's one of the few that remembers anything about that day before the shootings happened. Swears up and down he saw Jake at the house before the boys were shot. George, on the other hand, claims his brother was herding horses into town when he heard shots—insisted his brother arrived only after he'd killed the

Coffmans. One of 'em is lying. I believe Smithers over George."

This detail always struck Rogers as odd. Jake Villalba had been charged with complicity based on the statements of one man, an Anglo.

Just then young attorney Crawford peeked into the office.

"You back already?" Rogers asked, surprised to see Crawford back so soon.

"I've been gone two hours," he said.

Rogers pulled his pocket watch out and flipped open the cover. "Damn, I'd lost track of time. You already talked to both men?"

"Sure did. You about done?" Crawford asked.

"Just one more question, and I'll be done."

"I'll wait for you outside," Crawford said, surveying the unkempt office.

Rogers turned back to face Cartledge. "Knowing that the boys might do something stupid after they left your office the night before they were killed, why didn't you put them in protective custody, or at a minimum, have them escorted out of town?" Rogers asked, anticipating a convoluted self-serving answer.

Cartledge paused for a long moment then took another sip out of the nasty looking mug. His answer surprised Rogers.

"I screwed up, I know. Feel bad about it. The boys might still be alive if I hadn't been so trusting."

Rogers found himself consoling Cartledge. "Yeah, but for how much longer? They were bound to be killed by someone, the way they were stormin' around. It just so happened they picked one of the Villalbas to do the dirty work." Rogers hadn't been the first to come to this conclusion. He wouldn't be the last.

Cartledge had done little to shed new light on the case. He did confirm one thing, however. He was going to be a good witness for the defense.

"How'd it go with Florentino and the other gentleman?" Rogers asked as they walked back to the car.

"Good."

"Tell me first about Florentino."

"He said all the boys talked about the night before was about wanting to kill Villalba."

"Did he tell you where we might be able find the girls that were with the brothers when they went to the house?"

"He told me about the *jacales* the prostitutes live in over by the cemetery. Thought they might live there. I drove out there. No one has seen hide or hair of them since that day. Nobody could, or would, tell me where they had gone. The ladies didn't even go back to pick up their things. Apparently, all of the women's belongings remained in their shanty for days after the shootings before someone slipped in undetected and took them."

"What about the *cantinero*? What does he have to say?"

"He told me everything that happened the night of the card game."

"Had he seen the Coffman boys before or after the card game?"

"No. That was the first and last time he saw them. He laughed almost the entire time he told me the story." Crawford smiled. "Claims the younger brother actually pissed his pants when he put the shotgun to his head. I could barely understand what he was saying through all his laughter."

Over the ensuing weeks, all potential witnesses were interviewed. Rogers, accompanied by Charles Mead, met with the sheriff, and later with D.A. Montague to compare notes. In due course, eighteen witnesses were selected to testify for the defense.

Witnesses included Robert Cartledge, Sheriff Townsend, and W. D. Burcham, a mining engineer, community activist and self-proclaimed anthropologist who would testify about the polarization of the community.

It was agreed by opposing counsels that E. M. Gleim and Dr. R. A. Wilson would be called as state's witnesses. It had to appear that prosecutor Montague had some firepower in his arsenal; otherwise Dan Coffman might feel he had cause to take the law into his own hands. The Coffman brothers were acorns that hadn't fallen far from the tree. Everyone knew Dan was very capable of causing great harm if provoked. Two of his sons had been slain in a gunfight. Anything might happen.

14

The Murder Trial

The trial began on February 28, 1924. The crowd milling around in front of the red brick, two-story courthouse grew as word spread that the Villalba family would be present for jury selection. The windows, set in pairs with cornices like eyebrows, stood vigil over the multitude, as did the many eyes within. Sheriff Townsend knew full well that half of the Big Bend was gunning for Jacobo and Jorge. Jorge was in the Alpine jail in protective custody while Federico had ordered Jacobo to stay out of sight until he was called to testify. Golla's kin in Alpine saw to Jacobo's concealment. Only the most ignorant thought that Jorge and Jacobo would be displayed for a target shoot. Some in the crowd, however, would be plenty happy to settle for any one of the Villalbas.

In addition to the vigilant eyes he had in the courthouse, Townsend deputized twenty or so men to wander among the curious throng to make certain no one with a weapon slipped through. He also placed men on the corners of every rooftop surrounding the courthouse.

Only the principals in the case and prospective jurors were allowed into the courthouse. One by one, fifty or so citizens were admitted into the small courtroom on the second floor, but only after each was closely examined and patted down for weapons by the bailiffs. As the potential jurors entered to take their seats,

Brewster County Courthouse

defense attorney Charles Mead stood up, buttoned his navy blue pinstriped double-breasted coat and studied each face that passed in front of him. Montague, joined by County Attorney John Perkins, also stood up to greet the good citizens who shuffled in, nodding and smiling at those that looked his way. Some glared at whichever attorney they made eye contact with to let them know right from the beginning that this was somewhere they'd rather not be. Most others just looked over and smiled. A few recognized one or the other attorney and waved. Each attorney made a mental note of the transgressors.

The county clerk was present to check each jury summons a second time. Having been counseled by the sheriff, presiding Judge C. R. Sutton of the 83rd Judicial District wanted to make certain only invitees came to this dance. Federico, the only Villalba who came, entered unseen through the back door. He was allowed to sit next to his son at the defense counsel's table.

"Oyez, oyez, oyez, Court of the 83rd Judicial District is now in session," the bailiff shouted, as the judge entered the courtroom.

"Please be seated," the judge said, carrying the Villalba file in hand. He surveyed the courtroom. "Good morning everyone," the judge said, taking time to nod towards each counsel table.

"Good morning, your honor," the assemblage chorused.

The list of prospective jurors, with not one Mexican name or woman on it, was handed to Judge Sutton for his inspection. Copies of the list were handed to the attorneys.

"What about this one, Edith?" he asked, looking at his clerk and at a name she'd lined through.

"He's dead, your honor."

"Good reason not to be here," the judge said. Edith would have made the notation, but she knew the judge didn't like anyone's writing but his own on his jury lists.

Whispering among the prospective jurors quickly reached a low roar. The judge struck his gavel loudly to get everyone's attention.

"This is a court of law," he proclaimed, to the startled crowd. "You're not here to catch up on the latest gossip. The next person I hear talk while I'm trying to conduct business will be held in contempt and fined. Is that understood?"

Defense attorney Mead continued to study the jurors, looking for restrained hints of predisposition. This would be a racially charged trial. Anyone he spotted who appeared angry would be the first to go when he questioned the jurors. Judge Sutton formally welcomed the jurors. He introduced each attorney and spent considerable time explaining the nature and gravity of the charges. He explained that the attorneys would be given the opportunity to question them by way of a process called *voir dire*.

"Before the questions, I need to know how many of you can't stick around because of prior commitments."

Almost all of the fifty hands shot up. "I see," the judge remarked. "Looks like we got us some busy people here; all of you put your hands down. I warn you, if you raise your hand, you better have a damn good reason for wanting to be excused."

The judge's admonition had its intended effect. Only half the hands went up this time. A 72-year-old man, Bill Cunningham, was the first to be asked to stand and state the reason why he couldn't serve.

"The wife's pregnant your honor."

Giggles swept over the courtroom. Judge Sutton tried, but was unable to suppress a smile. "You're not lying to me, sir?" The judge asked.

"No, your honor. She's due next week," he said.

Someone from the back of the room decided to help Bill out. "He ain't lyin', judge. He married a young'un bout a year ago!" an anonymous voice shouted.

"Well, God Bless you, sir. Get outta here and go tend to the missus," the judge ordered. The rest of you will have to talk the attorneys into letting you go during voir dire. The judge then glanced over to his clerk. "Edith, go ahead and call up the jury panel in their assigned numerical order."

After a wince, shucks, damn or some other sort of reaction to having their name called, each juror made his way to his assigned chair.

"Y'all comfortable?" The judge asked of the jurors.

After a mixture of nods and yeses, the judge turned his attention to the District Attorney.

"Mr. Montague, you've got first crack. When the time comes, you'll have ten strikes," the judge said, obligatorily reminding the attorneys of the number of peremptory challenges each had to rid themselves of unwanted jurors.

Montague knew most of the jurors. He asked a few safe questions of each prospective juror and was done in short order.

Judge Sutton grabbed his gavel by the fat end and aimed the handle towards attorney Mead. "You're up counselor."

Mead knew what Montague was up to. The last thing he wanted was a jury made up of "good ole boys". If he didn't sort through these prospects with some hard questions, that's exactly what he would wind up with.

Mead stood up and re-explained voir dire...his way. He described the process more prosaically; didn't use the French pronunciation or these folks might think he was "puttin' on airs."

He moved towards the jury panel and looked down at his notes. He lightly penciled in a checkmark next to Mr. Ackerman's name.

"Mr. Ackerman, do you know the defendant Jorge Villalba or any of Mr. Villalba's family?" Mead asked.

"No sir, don't believe I do."

"Did you know either of the two young men who were killed?

"No sir."

"Do you know Dan Coffman their father?"

"No sir."

"Sir, may I call you Horace?"

"Sure, all my friends do."

"Thank you; I consider it a privilege that you would allow me to call you by your first name." Mead paused for a few seconds before continuing. "Do you have any children?"

"I do; four grown boys."

"Are they all living sir?"

"Thank God, yes."

"Any grandchildren?"

"Yes sir, two."

"Tell me, how do you feel about someone taking another's life?" Mead asked, jumping from children to the issue at hand.

"It's a bad thing," Horace answered with a serious look on his face.

"Have you ever killed a man?"

"No sir!"

"Do you think there is ever a good reason to kill someone?" Mead asked.

"In a war, I guess."

"How about outside of war? If someone was shooting at you, and you had a gun, would you shoot back?"

"Sure, who wouldn't?"

"Would you shoot to kill?"

"I'm not that great a shot. I don't know if I'd kill anyone, but that'd sure be my intent," Ackerman answered.

"One final question, how do you feel about Mexican people?"

"They're good people. Hard workers."

"Thank you sir.

Archibald Allen was next to be questioned. Mead asked essentially the same questions of Mr. Allen, with a slight twist.

"Mr. Allen, you say you have a young son and a daughter."

"I do."

"I'm sure you love them dearly."

"With all my heart," he said.

"Would you give your life for them?"

"I sure would," he responded with little hesitation.

"Would you take a life for them?"

"I'm not sure I know what you're asking," he said, cocking his head to his right and frowning in reaction to what he felt was an odd question.

"I mean, if someone were shooting in the direction of your children and if you had a gun, would you shoot the person who was doing the shooting?"

"Of course I would."

"Would you shoot to kill?" he asked.

"Yes."

"My next question may seem a bit unsettling, but in the best interest of my client, I must ask it. In this hypothetical situation, if the person you killed, while defending your children's life was Mexican, would you feel any more or any less distressed that you'd taken someone's life?"

"They bleed red just like we do. Taking a human life would be horrible, regardless of the color of their skin."

Mead had similar queries for the other prospects. Both attorneys submitted their lists of striken prospective jurors by midday. Thus, the twelve jurors and three alternates were selected. The jury was impaneled by two o'clock. The judge then called for a short lunch break.

15

A Tense Courtroom

After months of preparation, it was time to go to war. Mead reviewed his opening statement notes over lunch with his client's family. He looked up from his notes over his reading glasses as he set his coffee cup on the saucer.

"Fred, you understand that Montague is going to be saying some ugly things about Jorge and maybe even the family. He is going to make him out to be a heartless killer. I want this jury to see you and your son as the decent folk that you are. Just be yourself. We are on the right side of this fight. Don't lose sight of that."

"You don't have to concern yourself with my demeanor, Mr. Mead," Federico said with a distinct tone of self-assuredness. "I know what is true and what is not."

It suddenly dawned on Mead that Federico's daughter was missing. "By the way, where is your daughter?" he asked.

"She has left our home," Federico said.

By the solemn, almost angry look on Federico's face, and the uneasy look on the rest of the family's faces, Mead decided not to pursue the matter.

Miguel and Regina had traveled to El Paso where Miguel took a job as an insurance agent. Regina's heart ached with all that was happening between her and her father and with what was happening to Jorge. Her brother, Felipe, had offered to take her to Alpine with him for the trial. He did not, however, extend the offer to Miguel. Miguel knew he was *persona non grata* among the Villalbas. Miguel thought it best to stay away. He insisted Regina go. She was six months pregnant but perfectly able to travel. She refused to go without her husband. Regina cried herself to sleep for many nights to come.

Thanks to Sheriff Townsend and Judge Sutton, the Villalbas had an opportunity to meet with Jorge in the judge's chambers. They spoke for a long while until the bailiff came to collect Jorge and escort him to the courtroom. Two deputies stood at the back of the courtroom to make certain no one was able to get past the second row and to the Villalbas. Remarks muttered under breath left little doubt that most of the spectators were here to see a Mexican come to justice for killing two Anglos.

Most folks believed the Coffman brothers to be good boys. Maybe they got into mischief now and then, but no more than usual for boys who were brought up in some of the meanest land in the country.

A cheeky fellow in the middle of the fourth row, purposely or not, spoke loudly enough for the entire courtroom to hear.

"Ain't no Mexican worth all this attention unlessin' he's at the end of a rope."

Judge Sutton took notice and quick action. "Bailiff, kindly escort our orator in the fourth row out of my courtroom." The judge addressed the remaining spectators with a look that would have made the devil fidget.

"The rest of you listen up. From this point on, all I want to hear from y'all is yer breathin'. If I so much as hear a whisper, I will clear the courtroom."

Judge Sutton took a deep breath and a sip of water before continuing. "Mr. Mead, you ready for your opening statement, and are all your witnesses here?"

"I am, and they are all here your honor."

"Mr. Montague?"

"Yes, to both questions your honor," the district attorney said.

The Judge ordered the bailiff to read the charges.

"Jorge Billalba [sic], on or about the 25th day of May, One Thousand Nine Hundred and twenty-three and anterior to the presentment of this Indictment, in the county of Brewster and State of Texas, did then and there unlawfully and with malice aforethought kill Winslow Coffman, by then and there shooting him the said Winslow Coffman with a gun. How does defendant plead?"

Both Jorge and Mead stood up. "Not guilty," Jorge announced.

"You're up to bat, Mr. Montague."

"Thank you, your honor." Montague said. "Gentleman of the jury, I am here to seek justice—justice for a young man whose life was snuffed out in its prime. My purpose now is to give you an overview of what I intend to prove.

"I am here to tell you that I will be providing witnesses that will prove that Winslow Coffman did not go with his brother Jack to see George Villalba with the intention of killing him. They went there to scare him, to let him know they were not happy that George and his father conspired to have him and his brother fired so he could have their jobs."

"Objection, Mr. Villalba senior is not on trial here!" Mead bellowed.

"Sustained. Mr. Montague, please restrict your comments to the defendant."

Montague paused for a moment before continuing.

"I will prove that George Villalba did not have sufficient reason to grab his pistols and maliciously and cold heartedly shoot Winslow Coffman dead.

"Evidence will show that neither George Villalba nor his family was in any eminent danger because Winslow was not aiming at the defendant or his daughter. Witnesses will provide testimony that will show that Winslow was an excellent marksman. If he'd wanted to harm Mr. Villalba, he could have done it with his first shot. Winslow Coffman was there as a prankster not as an assassin, as the defense will undoubtedly ask you to believe.

"There were two witnesses to this tragic event. They, unfortunately, are nowhere to be found. We are going to have to rely on facts that lead up to what I will refer to as the act, and physical evidence that was collected after the act. Once everything has been put in front of you fine gentlemen, you will be asked to carefully analyze the information and determine guilt or innocence. There is no question that George Villalba killed Winslow Coffman, and after the evidence and testimony the State will provide, I am confident that you will find Mr. Villalba guilty of murder."

Montague glanced at Dan Coffman as he walked back to his chair. It was hard to tell by the expressionless face whether or not he was satisfied with the opening remarks.

"Mr. Mead," the judge said, nodding at defense counsel.

"Thank you, your honor. Gentleman, pay heed to what you have just been promised by the State. Mr. Montague has undertaken to prove three things beyond a reasonable doubt during this trial. One, that Mr. Villalba did not have 'sufficient cause' to grab his pistols and shoot Winslow Coffman dead; two, that neither he nor his family were in 'eminent danger'; and three, that the Coffman brothers were pranksters, not gangsters.

"Remember those promises, gentlemen. At the conclusion of this trial, after you've heard all of the testimony and examined the physical evidence, you're going to be called on to judge whether those promises were kept. I'll remind you."

Mead reached up and put his right hand over his heart to underscore the honesty of his words. He knew all the tricks and he fully intended on using them.

"In truth, gentlemen, the evidence is going to establish that on the afternoon of May 25th, 1923, my client was sitting on the porch of his home, in the company of his 4-year-old daughter. The Coffman brothers drove up and with guns drawn, walked up the front walkway and began shooting as my client came out to greet them. These brothers were aiming to kill, not to scare. After you hear and examine all of the testimony and evidence, gentlemen, you're going to wonder why this case was ever prosecuted. Fact is, this is almost like a second assault on my client's family.

"This is a most important case. Its outcome will affect not only the Villalba family, but will announce to the world how we, as a community, feel about our right to defend our homes and families."

16

The District Attorney's Case

The State's first witness was Dan Coffman. He characterized his sons' misdoings as "monkeyshines" worthy of a "good whippin', not gettin' killed." When asked about his sons shooting skills, he said he'd never seen his boys "miss anything they were shootin' at."

During cross-examination, he admitted that he'd never been around his boys when they'd been drinking.

"Mr. Coffman, were you aware that your boys had quite a reputation for being heavy drinkers?" Mead asked.

"My boys may have drunk a bit too much from time to time, but they weren't drunks, if that's what you're saying."

"Did either of your sons ever tell you that they 'drank a bit too much,' as you put it and Winslow was stabbed after starting a fight at a dance in town?"

"Yeah, they told me. Said some Mexican started the fight and Winslow was stabbed when he wasn't lookin'."

"Sir, are you sure you didn't hear about the stabbing from someone other than your sons?"

"Callin' me a liar?" Coffman asked.

Mead had Dan Coffman just where he wanted him. The jury was getting a clear picture of how little he knew of his sons' activities. "No sir, I'm just asking if you're absolutely certain your boys were the first to tell you about the stabbing."

"I'm sure."

"Mr. Coffman, are you aware of a card game involving Jorge Villalba where your son Jack bet and lost the family truck?"

"There wasn't no card game," Coffman said. "They sold the truck to old Fred."

"Did you know, sir, that your boys fabricated promissory notes, forged Jorge's signature not only for the truck, but also for a typewriter, and a supposed loan they made to Jorge's father, Federico? This way they could account for money they lost at cards."

"That's a bald-faced lie!" Coffman said. "My boys wouldn't do that."

Montague knew he was going to have to do some heavy damage control. He started jotting down notes as he listened to Mead pummel his witness.

"Mr. Coffman, you were invited to meet with Mr. E. M. Gleim and his brother, G. W., in Fort Davis to discuss some changes that were going to be made at the Texas Almaden Mine that involved your sons—is that correct?"

"Yes."

"Did you go, sir?"

"I knew they were gettin' ready to fire my boys—didn't need to go just to hear them tell me that," he answered.

"So your answer is no?"

"That's right. I didn't go."

"Were you aware that, at the time, Mr. Gleim was in negotiations with Mr. Villalba to merge their two stores for financial reasons?"

"All I know is Fred Villalba had been talkin' to them about wanting the job for his son, George. That's all I know."

"Sir, were you ever made aware of any other run-ins your boys had with the law while they lived in Terlingua?"

"Like I said, my boys were mischievous."

"Would you categorize pistol whipping a defenseless farmer nearly to death as mere mischief?"

"Objection, argumentative," Montague said.

"Overruled," said the judge.

"My boys didn't beat the man 'nearly to death' as you say. They might of roughed him up a bit but only because the old Mexican spit and cussed at them."

"How did you find out about the incident?"

"Don't remember. Just heard about it."

"You made a few trips from Shafter, where you live, to Terlingua after the incident. Is that correct?"

"I did."

Did you ever make it a point to discuss the incident with Terlingua Justice of the Peace, Robert Cartledge?"

"Nope. My boys had wrote me back and told me what'd happened. I didn't need to talk to Cartledge."

"Thank you, sir. I have no further questions."

"Any redirect?" the judge asked Montague.

"Yes, your honor," the prosecutor said as he stood up and approached the witness stand. "Mr. Coffman, do you know the Villalbas personally?"

"No—not really. I'd run into Fred and his boys on occasion, but never struck up any kind of friendship."

"Have your boys ever written or talked to you about the Villalbas?"

"Yeah. My boys said they were all hot heads and troublemakers, especially that young one, Jake."

"Did Ed Gleim ever talk to you about your boys' behavior?"

"Never."

"Did you ever receive any correspondence from Robert Cartledge advising you of problems he was having with your boys?"

"Nope."

"No further questions your honor." Montague strolled back to his chair.

Mead had chipped away at the Coffman myth and felt good about it. It was a good start.

"Next witness," Judge Sutton ordered.

Montague called Edgar Gleim. When asked about his friendship with the Coffmans, Gleim spoke fondly and charitably about the boys and their father. He felt responsible for what ultimately had gotten the boys killed.

When it was time for cross-examination, Mead pushed himself away from the table with both hands and stood up slowly. With both thumbs hooked in his vest pocket, he approached the witness stand, all the while, staring intently into Gleim's eyes.

"Mr. Gleim, didn't you have a conversation with the elder Mr. Villalba about the boys?"

"I did."

"I believe you told Federico that you had made a mistake in hiring Jack and Winslow Coffman, isn't that correct?"

"I may have said that."

"May have?" Mead prodded.

"I said it."

"What made you think you'd made a mistake?"

"The boys had gotten in trouble several times."

"With you or with the law?"

"With the law."

"How would you typically find out about these troubles?"

"Bob Cartledge would tell me, or I'd hear stories around town."

"Discounting the stories you heard in town, approximately how many times did you hear from the Justice of the Peace?"

"Maybe, half a dozen."

"Did he tell you about them beating the old farmer?"

"Yes."

"And the stabbing?"

"That too."

"Did this affect their job in any way?"

"No—not really."

"Well, then why did you want to fire them?"

"Felt bad for the townspeople."

"You mean the Mexican townspeople, don't you?"

"Objection—leading," Montague snapped.

"Overruled."

"Yeah, I suppose," he answered.

"Mr. Gleim, would you characterize the Coffman brothers as a ticking time bomb?"

"Objection, counsel is putting words in the witness' mouth."

"You're not getting away with it this time counselor—sustained," the judge ruled.

"Let me rephrase the question. How would you characterize the Coffman brothers?"

There was a long pause before Gleim answered. "Ticking time bomb is a fair characterization," Gleim said.

Montague shook his head in frustration. He thought of objecting but knew it would do little good.

When asked by Mead, Gleim talked about the Texas Almaden Mine's financial situation and why he thought a merger with

Federico Villalba's operation would be beneficial to both. "My brother and I have a mining partnership with Fred that goes back a few years. We know him and his boys as good honest men. Combining the stores and using George to run the single store was a sound business decision, not a personal favor to Fred," Gleim said.

The D.A.'s attempt to vilify Jorge by way of the next eleven witnesses failed miserably. The State called their last witness, Dr. R. A. Wilson.

"Dr. Wilson, you were asked to attend to the Coffman brothers after they were shot, Montague asked. "Is that correct?"

"Yes, sir."

"How long after the shootings did you arrive?"

"Half an hour or so."

"Were you the first to arrive?"

"Hell no! Half the town got there before I did," he said.

"Were both boys dead?"

"Very dead."

"Where did you find the bodies?"

"Winslow was half on the steps, half on the porch. Jack was entirely on the porch."

"Can you describe their wounds, doctor?"

"Sure. They were through-and-through wounds, each at the heart."

"You're saying the bullets exited the bodies?"

"Yep—went clean through."

"At what distance would you say the boys were shot from?"

"They weren't shot on the porch, if that's what you're asking."

"Could you elaborate, doctor?"

"If they'd been shot at that close of a range, there would be muzzle flashes on the bodies."

"Did you happen to see any large collection of blood anywhere on the walkway leading to the porch?"

"Everything had been badly trampled. There were traces of blood everywhere in the yard and on the porch."

"Doctor, isn't it possible that the boys could have been shot in the back as they were running away and dragged back to the porch to appear as if that's where they'd been shot?"

Jacobo was visibly upset by the district attorney's assertion that the Coffmans had been shot in the back. Montague couldn't have angered Jacobo more if he'd called him a coward to his face.

Severita did not understand one word Montague had said. What, she *did* understand was Jacobo's body language. His clenched fists, the forward movement of his body and right boot were all telltale signs of aggression. He was like a bull ready to charge the matador. Severita quickly reached over and grabbed his elbow, pulling back firmly. Jacobo could have easily slipped her grasp, but didn't. Frustrated, he shook his head and scooted back on the bench muttering obscenities under his breath. *He'd deal with that sonofabitch, Montague some other day.*

The doctor answered Montague's question.

"No, to having been shot in the back, and yes, to having been carried or dragged to the porch."

"How can you be sure they weren't shot in the back?"

"The entry wounds were in the chest and the exit wounds in the back."

"Do you consider yourself an expert in bullet wounds doctor?"

"I've treated enough bullet wounds to know where they go in

and where they come out."

"Were you able to locate the bullets?"

"You'll have to ask Sheriff Townsend about that. I didn't bother looking for them. I just checked for vital signs and stuck around until the undertaker came."

"Thank you, doctor. I have no further questions."

Charles Mead could hardly contain himself waiting for Montague to finish so he could cross-examine Dr. Wilson.

"Dr. Wilson, when you arrived, do you remember seeing the boys' guns?"

"As I recall, Jack still had his gun in his hand. I don't honestly remember where Winslow's gun was. It wasn't in his hand, I know. I remember seeing it. I just don't remember exactly where."

"Did you see any bullet holes on the house?"

"Sure did. While I was waiting for the undertaker, I looked around and marveled at all the holes in the wall. It was a miracle George or his little girl weren't hit."

"Objection, your honor. Move to strike Dr. Wilson's last comment as prejudicial."

"Sustained. The jury will disregard Dr. Wilson's comments about any miracles," the judge instructed the jury.

"Doctor, exactly what is the difference between an entry and exit wound?" Mead continued.

"When a bullet hits its intended target, it expands upon entry." To illustrate, the doctor gathered then flicked five fingers on his right hand to simulate an explosion. "Most of the damage is done at that point. It does more damage as it travels through the mass. When it comes out the other end, the exit wound is larger than where it entered. Even if you couldn't tell the difference between one hole or the other, you could easily identify entry by the comparable amount of tissue damage."

"Thank you, doctor. I think you've given everyone here an education on bullet wounds. Dr. Wilson, did you have occasion to treat Winslow Coffman for a stabbing wound a few months back?"

"Sure did. Scoundrel got himself stabbed at a party."

"I hear that he gave you less than a cordial welcome when you and the Justice of the Peace arrived."

"He was a bit put out, if that's what you mean."

"What did he say to you?"

"I don't want to repeat what he said in front of the women folk in the courtroom. Let's just say that had he been in better shape, and he'd talked to me that way, I'd a slapped him silly."

"Didn't you start to walk out and nearly refuse to treat Winslow because of the things he said to you?"

"I came back. I just needed to cool off. The kid was drunk. I don't suppose he'd a talked to me that way if he'd been sober."

"Did you have occasion to relate the incident to Dan Coffman?"

"Yup. Got home that night and wrote him a letter directly. Told him I didn't appreciate his boy's disrespect and asked him to have a talk with Winslow."

"Did Mr. Coffman ever respond to your letter?"

"Really didn't expect him to. Just wanted to let him know he needed to have a heart-to-heart with his boy."

"Thank you, doctor. No further questions."

"Any redirect, Mr. Montague?"

"Just one question, your honor."

"Doctor, how can you be sure Mr. Coffman received the letter?"

"Letter didn't go by pony express," the doctor joked. "I'm pretty sure he got it."

Dan Coffman could be seen squirming in his chair as the doctor testified. He was caught in a lie. He glanced toward the jurors. Several were looking at him with scowls on their face. He did his best to appear undaunted by the doctor's revelation and the jurors' scrutiny.

"Mr. Montague, according to my list, Dr. Wilson was the last of your witnesses," the judge said.

"That's correct, sir."

"In that case, I think I'm going to call it a day. Mr. Mead, you okay with getting started with your witnesses first thing in the morning?"

"That's fine with me, your honor."

The hollow sounding smack of Judge Sutton's gavel drew everyone's attention to the front of the courtroom. "Court is adjourned until nine Monday morning. See y'all then."

Jorge was returned to the Alpine jail behind the courthouse. It was nearly sunset. Loneliness would be setting in and so would the desert cold. A horse blanket in his jail cell did little to retain Jorge's body heat. The cold did one good thing. It took Jorge's mind off the foul-smelling remnants of someone's angry bowels. There were chamber pots in each cell. Jorge wouldn't use them unless it was to piss in. He forced himself to wait until morning to otherwise relieve himself. Sheriff Townsend made an exception and would let Jorge use the courthouse facilities.

Federico, his four sons and the attorneys retired to attorney Owen's study after dinner. Their host, Cassius "Cash" Owens, the most prominent attorney in Alpine, knew everyone and represented the well-to-do of the Big Bend area. Mead arranged to retain him as local counsel. It always helped to have a respected and familiar face at counsel's table. Although Mead was well known in West Texas, Owens had a friendly relationship with Judge Sutton and on this morning, it seemed with all the citizenry of Alpine. He had done well to buy this insurance against getting "hometowned" by the prosecutor and the judge.

Mead asked him to be present through jury selection as a third set of eyes. Maybe he'd catch some juror's telltale body movement or subtle gesture he or his associate missed that would give cause for a more intense scrutiny. Jacobo had arrived earlier in the day but stayed away from the courthouse, at Mead's request. He would take the witness stand Monday. Cash's wife, Elizabeth, entertained the women and children in the parlor as the men pored over the list of witnesses, eighteen in all. Federico was the first. Jorge the last.

Brewster County jail in Alpine

"Fred, how do you feel the trial is going so far?" Mead asked as he chewed his cigar.

Federico looked at Mead for a second or two. "I'm pleased," he said with a tired smile.

"So am I. Monday might be the clincher. Monty's assured me that his cross-examination of you and your son will be kept to a minimum. At this point, there's little he can prove up that will bolster his case."

"It took a lot less time than I thought it would," Federico reflected.

"No one is more surprised than I, except possibly for the judge," Mead said.

"Why the judge?" Federico asked.

"It's the first time he's ever had Monty and me in his court-room where we weren't in a dogfight—you know, at each other's throat."

The Villalbas kept a low profile over the weekend. Elizabeth Owens was a gracious hostess. Felipe and Jorge's children played together, their youth shielding them from the anxiety that weighed on Federico and the Villalba family.

17

The Defense's Case

For Federico and Severita, the third day of the trial began with a prayer and a *promesa* to San Federico, his patron saint. He promised to fast and pray for a week if his son was exonerated. He'd made promises before, but none more meaningful than this one, except for the one he'd made when his wife, María, was ill. He hoped he would be able keep his promise this time.

Federico stood in front of the witness stand uneasy with all of the attention he was getting. His weathered, callused hand blended into the brown leather cover of the Bible he placed his hand on.

The courtroom was warm. Federico's suit jacket, even unbuttoned, was binding and uncomfortable. It was the suit he had bought for his wedding to Severita a little more than a year and thirty pounds ago.

"Do you swear to tell the truth, the whole truth and nothing but the truth, so help you God?" the clerk asked.

"I do," Federico said.

Federico answered every question fastidiously and eloquently, recounting details of every conversation he'd had with Edgar Gleim. Montague had no success in poking holes in his testimony.

Jorge's wife, Golla, was called. She told of the terror she felt when the bullets started flying. She tearfully shared her horrified reaction at seeing her daughter outside, hiding behind Jorge as the

Coffmans came up the walkway with two blazing guns.

"I honestly thought these men were going to kill us and our babies. It was a miracle my husband and my daughter weren't killed."

During cross-examination, Montague again injected the notion that the brothers were actually running away.

"Mrs. Villalba, isn't it true that once your husband retrieved his pistols and pointed them at the Coffman brothers, that the brothers turned to run away, and isn't it also true that at one point Jack and Winslow looked back towards your husband, possibly to protect themselves, at which time your husband fired his weapons hitting them both in the chest?"

Golla was amused that the prosecution never picked up on who the real shooter was, and even more amused by Montague's farfetched and laughable attempt to make the Villalbas the aggressors.

Her answer would be the truth. "From where I stood sir, I never saw the men's backs until after they hit the ground."

Robert Cartledge was called to the stand.

"Mr. Cartledge, when was the first time you had an encounter with the Coffman boys?" Mead asked.

"Wasn't too long after they'd taken the job at the Texas Almaden store and mine," he said.

"Can you tell us what it was about?"

"Oh, they'd gotten into a fight at one of them Mexican *bailes*. I had to go out there and drag them out of the dance hall."

"This happened more than once, didn't it?"

"Too damn many times, if you ask me," Cartledge said.

"I'm curious. Why didn't you ever jail the boys for their antics?"

"I don't know that it would have done any good."

"Didn't you feel pistol whipping an old defenseless Mexican farmer was reason enough to put the boys in jail?"

"Looking back, maybe I should have," Cartledge conceded.

Cartledge described his encounter with the boys the night before the shootings. He again expressed remorse for not having taken the Coffmans' threats more seriously.

"Honestly, I thought they were bluffing. I don't always get along with Fred Villalba, but I respect him and his family. They're honorable people. There's no question in my mind that if George could have avoided shooting the boys, he would have," Cartledge said.

It was highly evident that Montague had lost the battle early on. At this point in the trial, he was merely going through the motions. His assaults were reduced to the occasional meaningless skirmish.

The testimony of Florentino, the blind musician, turned out to be impenetrable. He testified that the Coffmans said that they were going to kill Jorge many times over before the boys passed out and he was able to slip away.

Montague was up against a deck that became even more stacked by the time Sheriff Townsend testified.

"Sheriff Townsend, how long have you known the Villalbas?" Mead asked.

"Gosh—a long time. I've known Fred thirty years, at least."

"Do you consider them law-abiding citizens?"

"Jacobo's gotten into a little trouble now and then, but nothing serious. The rest of the Villalbas have never had problems with the law."

"What can you tell us about the unfortunate death of Winslow Coffman?"

"There are no witness accounts, except for George Villalba's wife, as you know. From everything I've been able to make sense of, it's an open and shut case of self-defense. This never should have gone to trial."

"Objection, your honor," Montague said loudly. "Move to strike Sheriff Townsend's last comment. He is offering an opinion."

The judge was tempted to voice his agreement with the sheriff but decided it would certainly give cause for an appeal in the event of an acquittal. The last thing he wanted was for this case to resurface because of a judicial misstep. He sustained the objection.

"What do you make of my esteemed colleague's theory that Winslow was shot as he was running away?"

"Ain't no way it happened that way," Townsend said, shaking his head. "George admitted to me that he and Jacob moved the bodies to the porch. Their intent was to move the Coffman brothers into the house, out of sight. They were afraid that if any Anglo saw the boys lying dead out in the yard, they might start shooting up the place and bring harm to George's wife and family. There is no question in my mind that the boys were shot midway up the walkway."

"Did you check the Coffman brothers' weapons?"

"I sure did."

"How many rounds were expended in Winslow's?"

"His gun had one bullet left in it."

"By the way, where did you find his gun?"

"It was one or two feet from the foot of the stairs."

"Did you account for all of the bullets that were fired from Jack and Winslow's guns?"

"They were all embedded in the adobe walls of George's place—every one of them—eleven all together."

"Did it appear to you that the boys had been shooting to scare Mr. Villalba?"

"From where George tells me he was standing, some of those

shots didn't miss him by much. If he hadn't ducked once or twice, a couple of those bullets would surely have found their mark. It's pretty clear those boys were aiming to kill. They were just too drunk to do it."

"No further questions, your honor. I reserve the right for redirect," Mead said.

"Sheriff Townsend," Montague began, "how can you be one-hundred percent certain those bullets were meant to kill?"

"Every one of those shots was chest high. They were meant for George all right!" Townsend reiterated.

"Couldn't it have been that the boys were such good marksman that they purposely shot close to George but purposely missed to scare him all the more?"

"Even if that were true, George was doing so much bobbing and weaving, as fast as they were coming at him, it's only by the grace of God that he didn't step into one of them bullets. Surviving the boys' gunfire that day had nothing to do with marksmanship."

On that note, Montague concluded his questioning.

"Mr. Mead?"

"No redirect, your honor. I wish to call Jacobo Villalba to the stand," Mead said.

Excitement in the courtroom became palpable with Jacobo seated in the witness stand. That meant Jorge would follow. The rising murmurs filled the courtroom, and Judge Sutton picked up his gavel, at the ready to clear the courtroom as he'd threatened to do the day before.

There was dead silence as Mead began questioning Jacobo.

"Mr. Villalba, when did you first meet the Coffman brothers?" Mead asked.

"A year ago maybe. My brother, Jorge, and I went to the Texas Almaden to invite them to play poker with us," Jacobo answered.

"You went out of your way to invite them didn't you?"

"They were new in town. We wanted to see if they were any good at cards."

"Were they?" Mead asked.

"They were terrible," Jacobo answered, with a half-muted chuckle.

"Tell us what happened at that card game?"

"Jack and Winslow lost quite a bit of money. We called the game when neither brother had any money showing on the table. Jack insisted on playing one last hand, wanting to wager the truck. We didn't want to take the bet, but he persisted. He lost."

Dan Coffman stood up suddenly and leaned menacingly on the rail as he yelled at the top of his lungs.

"You lying Mexican. My boys sold you that truck. I got the paper to prove it!"

To prevent Coffman from making any further move towards the witness stand, the bailiff ran over to Coffman, grabbed him by the shoulders and pushed him from the railing towards the bench.

Judge Sutton pounded his gavel loudly as he addressed Coffman.

"Mr. Coffman, you will sit down and refrain from any further outbursts. If I hear one more word out of you, I will hold you in contempt and you will spend the remainder of this trial in jail. Do you understand me, sir?"

Coffman resisted the bailiff for a brief moment before relenting. "Yes, your honor, I understand," he said as he sat down. Coffman looked over at his wife whose face was buried in her hands. She was crying for her boys. All she had now were memories and those were being sullied with accounts of scurrilous behavior. She wanted it to end.

Mead waited for order to be restored.

"Were the brothers upset?"

"Yes. Jack called us cheaters and pulled a gun on us."

"Did either you or Jorge draw your guns?"

"I drew mine under the table. Benny, the *cantinero,* ran to the table before anything happened and put a shotgun to the back of Jack's head."

All eyes were on Coffman as testimony continued. He sat angry but restrained.

"What happened then?" Mead asked.

"He made Jack give Jorge the key to the truck and escorted the brothers out of the *cantina.*"

"Did you ever play cards with the boys again after that night?"

"No."

"Did you ever run into the brothers after that?"

"I'd see them at a distance from time to time, but I never talked to them again."

"Where were you at the precise moment your brother shot and killed the Coffman brothers?"

"I was herding some horses into the corrals next to the house when I heard gunfire coming from the direction of the front yard. I left the horses and hightailed in the direction of the shots. When I got there, I saw my brother standing over the Coffman brothers' bodies."

"After he told you what had happened, what did you do?"

"I helped him carry the bodies to the house."

"Why did you move the bodies?"

"Jorge thought we should get the bodies out of sight. A Mexican killing two Anglos, *malas noticias*, bad news. We thought leaving the bodies out there would just make things worse."

"Why did you leave them on the porch?"

"The curious were starting to gather around the house. At that point, we thought it better to gather the family and leave the house before things got crazy."

"Where did you go?"

"To Cartledge's house to let him know what had happened."

"I have no further questions."

Montague looked at his notes one last time before he stood up and approached the podium.

"Mr. Villalba, you've killed a man before haven't you?'

"Objection, irrelevant!" Mead shouted as he stood up, ramrod straight. "Jacobo is not on trial here."

"Sustained. Mr. Montague, I suggest you get as far away from this subject as is humanly possible," the judge said with a stern look on his face.

"Mr. Villalba, you claim you only had dealings with Jack and Winslow that one time at the card game."

"That's correct."

"Didn't you, in fact, run into them at a dance not too long after the card game, and didn't you send word to them to 'get the hell out of there unless they wanted to get shot'?"

Mead knew of the rumor and had questioned Jacobo about it early on. Rather than object to the question's irrelevancy, Mead decided to let Jacobo dispel the rumor in the presence of the jury.

"There was never any such encounter. Whoever told you that was lying. You don't see me at *bailes* on this side of the Río!" Jacobo replied emphatically.

"You are not being honest with this jury, Mr. Villalba?"

Jacobo shot a wry smile towards the District Attorney. "Bring this man to this courthouse that told you he saw me at a *baile*. Let's see if he has the *cojones* to re-tell his lie in front of *me* and the jury."

Montague glared at Jacobo while he searched for an adequate response. He found none.

There was enough of a lull that Judge Sutton spoke up. "Any further questions, Mr. Montague?"

A look of defeat accompanied Montague's answer. "No more questions, your honor," he said in a barely audible tone.

It was close to the noon hour. Judge Sutton would spare the District Attorney any further humiliation.

"Let's break for lunch," he ordered with a resounding tap of his gavel.

The courtroom immediately erupted in loud chatter. Jorge Villalba's name bounced around the crowd as spectators streamed out of the courthouse and onto the front lawn where more people waited for updates.

"Looks like old George Villalba's going to get off," an anonymous spectator said as Jacobo emerged from the courthouse.

"He does, and Dan Coffman's going to kill that Mexican!" another voice yelled back.

Flanked by deputies, the Villalbas slipped out the back as they had throughout the trial. As before, they were driven to attorney Owen's home. Federico hadn't eaten breakfast and wasn't much in the mood for lunch. He sat on the porch and smoked his pipe as the others ate lunch. Severita and his boys offered to stay with him. Federico insisted on being alone.

The afternoon session began with the courtroom spectators on their best behavior. Jorge was immediately called as the final witness for the defense.

Mead asked about Jorge's relationship with the Coffmans prior to their being killed.

"Outside of the card game, I really had no relationship with them."

"How about their father?"

"Mr. Dan Coffman would occasionally run out of items at the Texas Almaden store and come over and buy the items from me at my cost plus a couple of pennies and resell them at his store."

"Wouldn't it have been easier to just have the people come over to your store to see if you had the item?"

"I suppose. The thing is most Anglos wouldn't buy from a store owned by Mexicans."

"Could the same be said for Mexicans buying from an Anglo store?"

"No, they'd buy from an Anglo store sure enough, but can't. Mr. Coffman wouldn't give Mexicans credit, unless they worked at the mine."

"Isn't the mine closed down?"

"It is, but that didn't make any difference."

"Jorge, did you get a written communication from Jack Coffman prior to them coming to see you the day of the shootings?"

"I did. A few weeks back, I found a note stuck under the door of the store."

"What did it say?"

"He called me and my family 'thieving sonsofabitches' and threatened to kill me."

"Did you let anyone else see the note?"

"I was tempted to take it to Mr. Cartledge but decided against it."

"Why is that?"

"I didn't think he'd do anything about it."

"What did you wind up doing with the note?"

Jorge looked around the courtroom embarrassed at what he was about to reveal.

"I took it with me to the outhouse and wiped my ass with it."

A collective gasp spread through the courtroom. Mead walked to his briefcase, extracted a leather glove and then proceeded over to the clerk's desk where he picked up an envelope. He put the glove on, slid the thumb and forefinger of his right hand into the envelope and gingerly pulled out a badly stained piece of paper. The document pulled from the outhouse—cleaned up as best as could be—was still reminiscent of what it had been used for.

"Can we mark this defense exhibit I, your honor?"

"We'll call it that; I don't think Edith is going to want to touch it to mark it. Proceed, Mr. Mead," the judge said, looking curiously at the piece of paper.

"Is this the document?" Mead said, holding the paper at arm's length.

Jorge and half the courtroom laughed at Mead's antics.

"Yes, it is."

Mead read the note in its entirety. He offered the note to the jury for closer inspection. The jurors looked repulsed by the suggestion.

"Mr. Mead, I don't think you're going to get any takers. Why don't you just walk slowly in front of the jury box and let them take a good look at it from a respectable distance?" Judge Sutton suggested, shaking his head in amusement.

Once the jury had seen enough of the document, Mead put the note back in the envelope. After a quick glance at the jury box to see if he still had their attention, Mead continued his questioning.

"Did you fear for your life when the boys showed up at your house that day?"

"Not at first. I immediately saw they were drunk. I thought I could talk them back into their car."

"Do you feel bad about having shot and killed the Coffman brothers?"

"I feel terrible that the boys are dead."

"Do you feel there was any way of avoiding the shootings?"

Jorge lowered his head and answered after a long reflective sigh. "No."

Montague tried every which way to poke holes in Jorge's testimony. He abandoned the "running away" theory, instead focusing on the animosity between the Villalbas and the Coffman brothers.

"Mr. Villalba, you made it very clear to others that you didn't like the Coffman brothers."

"I don't know of anyone that did."

"We're not talking about everyone else. We're talking about you," the prosecutor pressed.

"No, I didn't like them," Jorge confessed.

"You didn't like them enough to kill them, isn't that so?"

"They were killed before they killed me and my daughter."

"I believe that the minute the boys pulled their guns—even before they started firing shots to scare you, you made up your mind that you were going to kill them. You gave them no quarter, no chance," Montague argued.

"Objection, your honor. Counsel is badgering the witness."

"Sustained. Mr. Montague, why don't you save your denunciations for your closing argument?" Judge Sutton directed.

"No further questions," Montague said, clearly upset.

Unmoved by the district attorney's indignation, Judge Sutton looked at his watch. "It's barely three o'clock. Let's take a fifteen minute break."

Closing Statements

Mead was prepared for his closing statement. Montague was not. The prosecutor's fifteen minutes were spent at his table pouring over his notes.

"Court is again in session," the bailiff announced. The last few spectators squeezed into their seats as the judge sat down.

"Mr. Montague, is the State ready with closing remarks?"

"As ready as we'll ever be, your honor." The prosecutor walked to the end of the jury box and gripped the rail with both hands and looked into the eyes of each juror, one by one.

"Gentleman of the jury, first of all, I want to thank you for having given us your undivided attention in this very important matter. I hope you are proud of having participated in the wonderful gift our constitution has provided us with, and that is our right to a fair trial. I know we've thrown a lot of information at you and I, for one, appreciate how attentive you've been.

"You've listened to no less that thirty-two witnesses tell you what they knew about this unfortunate incident. Except for the defendant and his family, not one of those individuals, however, was witness to the shootings. The fourteen witnesses the State produced all had one common thread that unified the accounts each of them shared with you—sort of like a patchwork quilt. Montague spent the next hour "revisiting" the State's witnesses' testimony.

"If you remember, in my opening remarks I told you the State was going to prove that Winslow Coffman did not go to George Villalba's home to do harm to him. He was angry, but angry enough to kill George—NO, NO, NO!

"You heard Winslow's father testify that his sons were excellent marksman. If they'd wanted to shoot Mr. Villalba, they could have. It's asking too much for you to believe that the brothers could fire eleven shots from fifteen feet at the furthest point with the intention of doing harm to Mr. Villalba and his daughter and yet not one of those bullets even came close to nicking Mr. Villalba or his daughter, much less killing him.

"You heard testimony from George Villalba himself saying that he didn't like the Coffman brothers. Killing the boys may not have been premeditated, but gentleman of the jury, I submit to you that George Villalba did not have cause to mortally wound Winslow and Jack Coffman.

"Keep in mind George had time to run in to his home and grab his pistols. At that point, the rules of the game changed. George Villalba now had the upper hand. He could have come out and made the boys get back in their car and leave; instead he viciously shot the brothers through the heart, executed them without even as much as a warning.

"Gentleman of the jury, they don't come much more coldhearted than this. Your verdict isn't going to bring Winslow or his brother back. It isn't going to mend Mr. and Mrs. Coffman's heart.

"What it will do is let justice reign. Your verdict can let people know that the law will not tolerate the killing of an innocent young man. Thank you."

Other than cross-examining lying sonsofabitches and other hostile witnesses, the closing argument was defense attorney Mead's favorite part of a trial. His ability to capture and keep a jury with his measured oratory and stinging irony was renowned. He relished the opportunity to dismantle a prosecutor's case by highlighting gaps and inconsistencies, by making nothing out of something. He was masterful. He was ruthless.

Trials are gladiatorial battles. Mead liked to look into his opponent's eyes when he inflicted a damaging blow. He loved watching as they squirmed in their seats. Prosecutors hated him for that.

After District Attorney Montague concluded his closing remarks, Mead slowly rose to his feet. He was an imposing presence in the courtroom; tall, well dressed. As he stared pensively at the jury, all eyes were on him and he knew it. He assumed a somber countenance and allowed some time to pass before addressing the jury. He had everyone's undivided attention as he stood in the center of the courtroom.

"Gentlemen of the jury. Friends, fathers, husbands and sons, all of us, we have just spent the better part of a week hearing the absolute best evidence that the great State of Texas could muster.

"And what have we heard? What evidence has the State furnished to establish in your mind, beyond a reasonable doubt, that on the 25th day of May 1923, Jorge Villalba 'did then and there unlawfully and with malice aforethought kill Winslow Coffman' as alleged in the indictment?"

Mead pretended to read from the indictment as he cast a furtive glance at the district attorney. Montague busied himself with shuffling papers at his table, pretending not to notice Mead's piercing glance. It was beginning. Montague hated Mead for personalizing these things.

Mead continued. "Let us assume for the sake of argument and brevity, the truth of the State's best case. Let us assume that it was, as the State contends, a prank or joke that prompted the Coffman brothers to raid the home of my client that day. A joke sired by whiskey mixed with a touch of malevolence and spawned in a saloon. Let us further assume, as the State contends, that these drunken brothers were not really intent on killing my client, just trying to scare him a bit and registering their displeasure at the loss of their jobs to him."

Mead pointed to his head, closed his eyes and cocked his head skyward.

"Visualize it in your mind: a beautiful, breezy spring afternoon. Mr. Villalba enjoying the day on the front porch of his home. With him is his precious four-year-old daughter, María. They're lazing in a chair where she has climbed up on his lap before dozing off after chatting with daddy. Mrs. Villalba is in the home tending to her other children and whatnots."

Mead glanced at the jury. They seemed hypnotized by the slow and deliberate cadence of his voice.

"Out of nowhere and with no discernment whatsoever that it's all a prank, the Coffman brothers drive up and spill out of their car, drunk, each armed with a pistol. They level their guns at Mr. Villalba who has come halfway up the walkway to greet them. The Coffmans start yelling obscenities and opened fire. Two guns blazing.

"Mind you gentlemen, this is his home with his entire family present. They riddle the porch with a fusillade of bullets while little María is now clinging to her daddy's leg, who is doing his best to shield her while dodging bullets."

Mead paused. "You heard the testimony of Sheriff Townsend. Eleven of the twelve bullets in the Coffmans' arsenal were found embedded in the front porch of the house.

"Now, ask yourself is there anything about these facts that you think would lead a reasonable man to believe that he and his family are amidst a harmless prank or elaborate joke? What would a reasonable man do in response to this onslaught on his home—laugh?"

Mead cast another glance at Montague who sat with his gaze affixed to the floor.

"This was no joke or laughing matter. There was nothing funny about the stark terror that my client's daughter, wife and other children felt as they cowered for what must have seemed like an eternity, bullets whirling about them. Those were not blanks these men were shooting.

"I ask you, how still and how long must you sit under such circumstances before raising a hand in your own defense?" he said, pointing at the jury members.

"What levels of force can you use? How can you defend yourselves? Thankfully, our law answers all these questions for us."

Some of the members of the jury scooted forward in their seats. They wanted answers to the questions Mead had so expertly made personal.

"His honor is going to instruct you that under our law, a man has an absolute right to defend himself, his property and his family from attack by using the same level of force as that being exerted against him. As fact finders, you will look at all the circumstances through the eyes of the defendant. Did he act reasonably? Was the level of force he used appropriate?

Mead paused once again, surveying each juror. Everyone was intent, entranced. He raised his voice a decibel to make sure the jurors followed him through the next door he was about to open.

"Gentlemen, do you believe there is any sane human being that could have confused that gunfire and those screams for a prank? I put it to you plain and frank, is there anyone amongst us who would not have reacted identically under the same circumstances? Is there anyone here who would have done nothing?" Mead pursed his lips and shook his head. He hooked his thumbs in his vest pockets. Those who knew him well recognized that he was about to strike another masterful blow.

"The only joke we've heard in this courtroom is the absurdity of the assertion in the State's case that the Coffman brothers stormed my client's home with the intent to only scare him. Scare him into what? Defending himself and his family? Recall Sheriff Townsend's testimony. Based upon his observations of the eleven bullets embedded in the porch, it was clear that the Coffmans were aiming to kill. They were all 'chest-high'. Those were his words gentlemen, not mine. He testified that Jorge Villalba was a law-abiding man.

Mead walked towards the witness stand, using it as a backdrop and a prop for the remarks that would follow.

"And what testimony did the State bring to you regarding the peaceful and law-abiding nature of the Coffman brothers? Just who were the Coffman brothers? And why are we here only trying the death of Winslow Coffman? Was his brother Jack, a lesser being? No, gentlemen. We are here on only one brother because the State doesn't want to have to defend Jack's famous penchant for guns, knives and violence."

"Objection, judge," said Montague. "Arguing outside the record."

"Sustained."

Mead let it go. He acted as though the judge had ruled in his favor.

"Thank you, your honor." He'd made his point to the jury. The district attorney couldn't un-ring that bell.

"Recall the testimony of Edgar Gleim, who, as their last employer probably knew the Coffman brothers better than anyone. Recall that he described the Coffmans as a 'ticking time bomb'.

"Recall the testimony of Justice of the Peace Robert Cartledge. Remember that his first encounter with the Coffman brothers was after they had been brawling at a *baile*. Remember his remorse at not having arrested them for pistol-whipping a defenseless old farmer to near-death merely because they claimed he insulted them. He also testified that he didn't think that arresting them would have made any difference.

"Remember that he was sorry that he had not taken their public threat to kill Jorge more seriously. That threat was issued the very night before these events. What does that tell you about their intentions once they were at my client's home, gentlemen?"

Mead excused himself and walked over to the defense table and poured himself a drink of water. He did it to let all absorb what he'd just said. After two sips and a wink of an eye at Jorge, he turned and faced the jury and continued.

"In contrast, Sheriff Townsend testified that in his opinion, based upon his knowledge of Jorge Villalba, there was no question in his mind that, if Jorge could have avoided shooting those boys, he would have. Sheriff Townsend has no dog in this fight, gentlemen. As a community, we trust him with the safety of our businesses, homes and families. We should place equal confidence in the truthfulness of his testimony."

Montague slid further down his chair as if attempting to hide.

It was over, and he knew it. In an embarrassing moment, he opened his eyes and looked towards Mead just as the defense counsel glanced towards him. He took the opening to cast an angry withering look towards Mead thinking, *you bastard.*

Mead walked to the far end of the jury box next to the vaulted window.

"So there you have it, gentlemen, the truth, the whole truth and nothing but the sacred truth. Not because I tell you so, but because all the credible testimony and physical evidence does. And just how do you discern the truth in this case, gentlemen?" Mead reached for the edge of the drapes and pulled them back.

"You see it from its source. You recognize it as you recognize the very sunlight that shines into this courtroom. It's pure, and it's simple, just like the facts of this case—and that is the very nature of our defense."

Meads gesture was as brilliant as the beams of sunlight. It was his way of introducing the jury to the divine illumination of the truth and the righteousness of his cause. He released the drapes and adjusted the tone of his voice.

"Now, gentlemen, I have carried the burden of defending my client since I undertook to represent him. During that time, I've come to know and respect Jorge and his family. I care deeply for them. I've been entrusted with Jorge's well being. I now have to transfer and entrust my client's well being to you as you prepare to deliberate.

"Think about this, gentlemen. You know so much more about Jorge than he knows about you, yet you are about to pass judgment upon and determine his fate.

"I'll tell you what Jorge does know about you. He knows that as law-abiding fathers, husbands and sons in our community, you work hard to build better lives for your children, family and loved ones. You toil day in and day out. You place the interest of your family above your own. And you would not hesitate to defend their life—even if it meant taking the life of an assailant. He takes comfort in that knowledge gentleman, because Jorge is no different. Regardless of the color of our skin, we share that common bond.

"I entrust Jorge to you, gentlemen. Do that which you know in your heart is right. Deliver him. May God's hand guide you in your work."

With that, he was done. Mead returned to his table and sat next to Jorge, gently patting his shoulder as if to say, "Everything's going to be all right."

"Any rebuttal, Mr. Montague?"

The D.A. looked at the judge and shook his head.

"None, your honor."

The Verdict

Judge Sutton whispered something behind his hand to the clerk who immediately left through the door that led into the judge's chambers. A minute later she returned with several sheets of paper. They turned out to be the judge's jury instructions that he had left in his chambers.

The judge cleared his throat, took a sip of water and then launched into a half hour of jury instructions. With that, he handed the instructions to give to the jury foreman and dispatched the jury into the deliberation room.

The spectators cleared out as the attorneys gathered their papers and stuffed them into their briefcases. Mead and Perkins were optimistic. Federico, on the other hand, was sure of what should happen, but couldn't bring himself to believe that a fair outcome would necessarily prevail. After all, this was a case of a Mexican killing an Anglo.

Fifteen minutes passed. Montague and his assistant left the courtroom; Mead and the others were about to leave when the door burst open.

"You people might want to stay put," the bailiff said, walking across the courtroom to the judge's chambers.

"There couldn't possibly be a verdict already," Mead said.

They all sat down. Minutes later, the bailiff exited the judge's chambers.

"The verdict's in," he said as he made his way past the defense table and out the double doors to look for Montague.

Federico was stunned, not knowing what to think or say. He looked over his shoulder at his wife and then across the bench at his sons who sat next to her in total wonderment. Just then the bailiff came back with Montague in tow.

Word of a verdict spread like wildfire. Spectators scampered back to their seats. Once everyone was back in place the bailiff left to retrieve the judge. Judge Sutton surveyed the courtroom before he instructed the bailiff to bring the jurors in.

The judge leaned forward and looked to the side at the jurors.

"Who was selected as foreman?"

"I was your honor." Arch Allen stood up and introduced himself.

"Mr. Allen, I understand the jury has reached a verdict."

"We have your honor."

"Go get it, Ben," the judge instructed the bailiff.

The jury foreman looked about the courtroom nervously. His gaze seemed fixed on Dan Coffman sitting in the front row on the aisle next to his friends. Mr. Allen felt a tug on the verdict form that had been folded in quarters, and he held securely between the thumb and forefinger of his right hand. He turned and looked at the bailiff, then released the document.

Ben strode to the bench and handed the form to the judge. The bailiff then positioned himself to the right of the judge to keep an eye on Dan Coffman, and a hand near the butt of his gun. He had a good hunch what the verdict would be and Dan Coffman's reaction to it.

Judge Sutton unfolded the form and inspected it for what seemed like an eternity to Jorge and his family. He handed the form to the clerk, J. W. Frazer, who read its contents.

"We, the jury, find the defendant not guilty."

The courtroom broke out in pandemonium. There were cheers from Jorge's family and jeers from a few spectators. The judge banged his gavel, yelling for order. His Honor motioned for the bailiff and the extra deputies to clear the courtroom. One deputy, assigned to keep an eye on Dan Coffman, quickly moved to block any visual access Coffman had to Jorge.

Once order had been restored, the clerk addressed the jury. "Gentlemen of the jury, is this your verdict?"

The jury responded in the affirmative.

Judge Sutton thanked the jurors for their service and dismissed them.

"Do we have to stick around for anything else?" the jury foreman asked.

"No, sir. You're free to go home," the judge replied.

The jurors left in haste, some taking one last glance at Dan Coffman to see if he'd remained seated.

Dan Coffman sat motionless, stunned at what he had just heard. He was fully aware of eyes watching his every move. As much as he wanted to jump over the rail and choke the life out of Jorge, he knew he would be restrained if he so much as twitched an eye. He didn't see any point in saying anything. He would reserve comment for those of his friends who he knew had the same opinion of Mexicans and of the Villalbas in particular. Maybe some day he would get his chance at exacting the style of justice he thought was proper. Dan Coffman took one last angry look at the Villalbas and walked out of the courtroom.

"Mr. Villalba, you're a free man. This court is adjourned," Judge Sutton said, giving his gavel a solid smack.

Federico and his family rushed to Jorge in jubilation. Charles Mead moved aside so the Villalbas could celebrate their victory.

"*Gracias,*" Federico said to Mead with tears in his eyes.

Jorge, who was hugging his stepmother and brothers, heard the exchange. He spun around to speak.

"*Sí, gracias por todo,* he said, barely able to talk for all of the emotion that had welled up in his throat.

"I was privileged to have been of help," Mead said, happy and relieved.

District Attorney Montague proceeded to the rooming house to pack and ready himself for his trip back to Marathon. On the way to his room, he saw Arch Allen, the jury foreman, who was on his way out. Arch stopped.

"Mr. Montague, why did you spend so much time with your closing speech when you didn't have a chance of winning?" he asked.

"Oh, I guess I just had to get it out of my system. But tell me something, Arch, why did it take so long to reach a verdict?" Montague asked playfully.

"Why Monty, it took us just one minute to reach the not guilty verdict. We spent the other fifteen minutes hoping Dan Coffman and his friends would get out of the courtroom and avoid trouble," Allen confided.

Montague recalled several tense and loud moments in the trial, thanks to Dan Coffman's hair-trigger temper.

"Several times we almost had a killing in that courtroom." He repeated himself a second time, then bid goodbye to Mr. Allen.

18

The Loss of Rancho Barras

Federico watched his family rejoice in Jorge's acquittal. In spite of the wonderful outcome, a pall was cast over his contentment by the stark realization that his family would return to a ranch that was no longer theirs.

Federico traveled to Marfa the next week to work out the details of Mead & Metcalfe's assumption of ownership and the role he would play in the management of Rancho Barras. His primary concern was his family and the effects the loss of the ranch would have on them.

Jorge had already decided he and his family would leave Terlingua and live in Big Spring where Golla had kin. Jacobo would remain and work his ranch in Santa Elena. Federico's estranged daughter, Regina, remained in El Paso, along with her brother Felipe. That left Santos, Lico and Severita to help run the ranch and the store.

Federico was anxious but not frightened about what was to come.

Regina received word via telegram that her brother had been acquitted.

"We should never have left," Regina said, reading the communiqué.

"It wasn't safe for you in Terlingua," said Miguel. He paused and thought for a long moment before continuing. "We'll head back after the baby comes along."

"I think that would be best," Regina agreed.

The Villalbas returned to Terlingua following the trial. This gave Federico time to keep his *promesa*. Jorge, in the meantime, made good on his plans to move to Big Spring.

"Papá, we must leave Terlingua. It is no longer safe or beneficial for me to remain. I hope you understand."

"My son, you and your family have been through a horrifying ordeal," Federico said. "Terlingua will hold harsh memories for you. We want you to be happy and your children to be safe. What you are doing is right for your family." Jorge's eyes moistened.

"I don't want you to feel that I am abandoning you, Papá."

"*Mi hijo*, that thought hasn't entered my mind. You are as brave a man as it has been my privilege to know. You are my son, but you are also a husband and father. Your family must come first.

"*Vaya con Dios*," Federico said, wiping his eyes with the back of his hand.

Jacobo stayed in Terlingua to see his brother off. For all these months, the younger Villalba had internalized the distress of not coming forward to assume the blame for killing the Coffmans. He knew the outcome of the trial would have been dramatically different had he done so. Even so, it did not sit well with him that he allowed Jorge to place himself in such jeopardy.

"*Manito*, it should have been me in court," Jacobo said.

Jorge looked at his brother and smiled.

"If it had been you, they'd 'ave hung your butt."

"I will miss you."

"I know you will," Jorge replied. "Who's going to keep you out of trouble?"

Jorge put his hand on Jacobo's shoulder and gave it a reassuring squeeze. "Don't worry *manito*. I'm not going that far. Come and see us from time to time—bring Carmelita. Perhaps we can find us some *tiernito* for a game of poker who we can teach the finer points of the game."

Jacobo laughed.

"*Adios*," Jorge said.

Jacobo embraced his brother. "*Adios*," he replied.

On the day of their appointment, Felipe and Federico left for Marfa early and arrived apprehensive. Mead greeted them and invited them into his office.

"You're early. How was the trip?"

Federico didn't much feel like making small talk.

"It was fine. Can we attend to the business at hand?" he asked impatiently.

"Surely, did you bring the deed?" Mead asked.

"We'll give it to you in due time," Felipe said. "First, we need to talk about the terms of your ownership."

"It's really very simple," Mead said. "We own the ranch and your family leases it back from us. I'd already talked to your father about it."

Felipe Villalba

"No, Mr. Mead, it's not that simple. You are assuming owner-ship of one of the most productive ranches in the Big Bend. A lease is just not acceptable."

"Well, what do you propose?" Mead asked, miffed at Felipe's assertiveness.

"I propose that you give my family 50 percent of the profit in addition to providing an additional 25 percent for operating costs."

"That's insane. That leaves us with 25 percent," Mead said in astonishment.

"The way I see it, 25 percent of something is quite a bit better than 100 percent of nothing."

"I don't follow you," Mead said.

"Perhaps I can best illustrate my point with a story. You, of course, know of Pancho Villa."

"Sure, who doesn't," Mead replied.

"Pancho had a horse that he called *Siete Leguas,* Seven Leagues in English. He was a gorgeous coal black stallion that stood eighteen hands. The horse's reputation was as renowned as Pancho's.

"One day Pancho and two of his men were riding outside of Ojinaga when a troop of *federales* spotted him. They caught Pancho off guard and were able to come within shooting distance. Three other men, who were also revolutionary soldiers and had never met *El General,* were camped nearby.

"They heard the gunfire and poked their heads over rocks to see what was happening. They jumped on their horses and rode to a position where they could take clear aim on the *federales.* Each hit a *federale* with their first shot. The *federales* left the area, abandoning their dead and wounded.

"After their good deed, the men returned to their campsite and set up for the night. Suddenly, they heard a noise in the dark. As they drew their weapons, a voice said, 'I am Pancho Villa. Permit me to enter your campsite.'

"They kept their guns drawn on the shadowy figures approaching on horseback. The face that emerged was indeed that of Pancho. He asked for the leader and a young man quickly stepped forward.

"Pancho thanked the man for saving their lives and told him he would give him anything that was within his power to give. Without any hesitation, the man asked him for his horse. Pancho told him he would gladly give him his horse but warned him that *Siete Leguas* was a one-man horse and could not be ridden by any other man.

Pancho Villa and Siete Leguas

'You don't know what a good horseman I am,' the young man said to Villa. With that he put his foot in the stirrup and the horse immediately reared up, throwing him to the ground. He tried mounting the horse several more times with the same result. With great embarrassment he handed the reins back to Villa. Pancho reached into his saddlebag and took out a piece of paper and scribbled something on it. 'Here is a deed to ten acres I own in Chihuahua. It's yours,' he said.

"Pancho and his men got on their horses and rode away, still chuckling at the young man's attempt to ride the legendary *Siete Leguas.*

"Mr. Mead, as Pancho warned the man, I am warning you.

Rancho Barras is a horse that can only be ridden by one man. This land was tamed by my father and it performs for him only."

Mead lit his cigar, puffed on it, and smiled.

"That's some story."

"It is a true story," Felipe assured the attorney.

"You drive a hard bargain, Felipe. If you ever want to leave El Paso and join my firm, there's a chair here with your name on it."

"I'm flattered, I'm perfectly happy where I am at," Felipe said, staring intently at Mead. "Are we in agreement?"

"We are." Clearly, Mead had been outgunned and knew it. "Now if I can have the deed."

Howard Perry

The Villalbas returned to Terlingua pleased at the outcome of the meeting. Upon their arrival, Severita told Federico of a visit from Ed Gleim.

"Don't tell me he's still considering a merger after everything that happened?" Federico said.

"That's not why he came. He wanted to tell you that Howard Perry wrote him inquiring about our financial situation and whether or not he was proceeding with the merger," Severita reported.

"That sonofabitch. He's probably hoping I have to close my doors."

"He's a businessman, Papá," Felipe said.

Federico's face flushed with anger.

"You couldn't possibly be defending the man."

"No, not at all. Let me ask you a question. If the shoe were on the other foot, would you have inquired about Perry's circumstance?" Felipe asked.

"I suppose I would have," Federico conceded. He had given great thought to what he would do with the Study Butte store.

"Shouldn't we shut down the store?"

"I can't. Perry doesn't give credit to our people. They need us," Federico said.

"But Papá, it's a money loser."

"They need us," he repeated.

Felipe knew better than to debate the issue. He knew his father would never give Howard Perry the satisfaction of knowing that Federico Villalba closed his doors because of any pressure El Perro might have applied.

Months passed. Adjustments were made. Federico missed his boys and his daughter. Lico and Santos had worked hard to assume more responsible roles in the management of the ranch.

Jacobo Returns to Bootlegging

The Chisos mine had been doing a reduced but steady business, eventually even firing up the rotary furnace that had been dormant for years. The Texas Almaden and some of the other small mines reopened. War-time production of mercury, however, was a bonanza that was never to be seen again. Times were changing.

For Jacobo, the business enterprise that continued to grow was measured in liters and alcoholic in nature. *Sotoleros* continued to do a booming business, expanding even beyond their expectations.

The lure of more money grew to be too much for Jacobo, who called Valentín and his uncles to his ranch in Santa Elena.

"Gentlemen, I have decided to re-involve myself with our exportation business," he announced.

"I don't see that we need you," Candelario said. "We have done just fine without you."

"You seem to forget that you would have no business if I had not given it to you. The people you are supplying contracted with me. The only reason they continued to do business with you is because I told them they could. Their loyalty is to me," Jacobo reminded Valentín's father, hoping Pablo was also paying mind to what he was saying.

Candelario was no fool. He knew that Jacobo could take the business back with or without his cooperation. If he resisted, all he would have left is fond memories. He decided to back off and let Jacobo reassume the leadership, but he wanted more too.

"We want a bigger percentage of the profit. We are due something for having kept the business alive while you were absent, and we want extra for the longer trips," Candelario demanded.

Jacobo didn't refute Candelario's logic or demand. It sounded fair.

"I will give you an extra five percent and an extra two percent for the longer trips." That brought the brothers' combined take to 37 percent. His deal with Valentín would be separate and concealed from the brothers.

"I suppose that will have to do," Candelario said. His plan had backfired, but he was pleased that Jacobo kept him in the business. It was more profitable and agreeable than goat ranching.

The relationship between the Villalbas and the Baizas became all the more strained. Candelario always took great enjoyment in knowing that most people feared him, except for the Villalbas.

This never sat well with him, nor did his knowing that Santos Villalba was now wooing Pablo's daughter, Isidora.

Federico found out soon enough of his son's growing reputation as one of the region's top bootleggers. There was little he could do to prevent his son's involvement. His protestations obviously fell on deaf ears. His only consolation was that Jacobo was protected by the Río Bravo and traveled into the Big Bend only when necessary. His life was now in Santa Elena with his ranch and his girlfriend, Carmelita.

The Bullet-Eater

Santos and Isidora's relationship hit a rough patch. He sought his father's advice. The advice was simple.

"*Mi hijo*, she isn't worth the trouble," Federico told his son.

Santos became infuriated. "Because she's a Baiza?"

"Any woman who cannot make her man happy isn't worth the trouble. This has nothing to do with her being a Baiza," Federico explained. "If she's this way now, imagine how she is going to be if you marry her."

"I love her, Papá."

"Well then, make it work. Lay the law down to her and quit your whimpering."

Santos rode across the river to visit his brother Jacobo in Santa Elena for consolation. He'd gotten little from his father. They sat and talked and drank for a while, long enough for Santos' emotional pain to dull, not to mention his senses and good judgment. He decided to take his father's advice and go to Pablo's house in town and once and for all let Isidora know who was boss.

He arrived, hollering from his horse, demanding that she come out. Isidora and several of her siblings looked out of the window and saw that Santos was drunk.

"Go home!" Isidora yelled. "*¡Estás borracho*, you are drunk!"

"Come outside woman!" Santos yelled.

Isidora's younger brother, Adolfo, became enraged at Santos' antics. Without telling anyone, he retreated to their father's bedroom and retrieved a rifle kept under the bed. By this time, Santos had started to climb the steps to the house while still on his horse.

"Come outside," Santos yelled. The sound of the horse's hooves on the porch was deafening. The ramshackle house shook under the horse's weight and movement. It made Adolfo all the angrier.

"Get away!" he yelled at his brothers and sisters.

They all turned, saw he held a rifle in his hands, and dove for cover. Isidora yelled for him to stop, but before she could reach her brother, he squeezed the trigger.

The bullet ripped through the door showering splinters over the children. The next sound the Baizas heard was a loud thud on the porch. Isidora opened the door and saw Santos lying on his side with blood pouring from his face and mouth.

She knelt and saw a hole in his cheek. The bullet had entered his cheek, but she couldn't see where it had come out. Santos was alive and breathing. Isidora was in a panic. Her mother was in town, and her father away on business. Isidora and Adolfo loaded Santos in the buckboard and rushed him to Dr. Wilson in town. For almost the entire trip into town, Isidora punched and slapped Adolfo's shoulder for having shot her boyfriend.

"Damn, what happened here?" Dr. Wilson asked Isidora. "This is old Fred Villalba's boy, isn't it?"

"His youngest, Santos. My brother shot him by accident,"

Isidora said, giving her brother a look that would melt the snow on the Christmas Mountains.

"Some accident. He's lucky to be alive," the doctor said.

Santos was starting to regain consciousness.

"Who hit me?" he asked.

"This was more than a right cross my good man. You had a bullet go clean through your cheek and out your neck," the doctor told Santos.

"Looks like you're going to be okay, but you're one lucky *hombre*; the bullet managed to miss everything that counts."

The doctor looked at Isidora and whispered, "If this young man weren't so drunk, he'd be writhing in pain. I sure as hell don't envy the boy. Soon as the liquor wears off he's going to be hurtin' a might and have one helluva hangover."

The closest hospital was in Alpine. The doctor didn't see the need to cart him that far. Miraculously, the bullet, a .30 caliber, had done little damage. He decided to send Santos home for recuperation. He cleaned the wound and applied a bandage.

"I'd better go with you. Fred and his wife need to know how to care for the wound so it doesn't get infected," he said. With that the doctor washed his hands, put on his coat and grabbed his medical bag.

Adolfo knew if he went with his sister he would be in hostile territory. He decided to go home to await a visit from the law.

Federico's initial alarm turned to anger when the details of what happened became clear. The doctor reported the incident to Robert Cartledge, who had his constable conduct a cursory investigation, deciding it was a matter best resolved by the two families. Federico told his sons to stay away from Adolfo.

Santos now had a new nickname. Everyone began calling him "*traga bala*," or bullet-eater.

Trouble with Charles Mead

Mead and Metcalfe began exerting pressure on Federico to cut back on ranch expenses. For Federico, their interference was hard to chew on and even harder to swallow. He needed more control of the finances, but he conceded that was a thing of the past. Each time an auditor came, recommendations followed, always to cut corners. Federico was accustomed to running the ranch aggressively. Mead and Metcalfe wanted maximum yield with minimum input. The ranch could no longer afford to support three households.

Federico knew his sons would never abandon him. He wrote to his friend, Herbert Lee Kokernot, to see if he might be looking for some good men for his O6 spread, asking if he might hire his two sons and Valentín Baiza.

"H. L." had taken over management of 300,000 acres in Brewster County a few years back. The Kokernots owned more than half a million acres in Jeff Davis, Pecos and Brewster counties. Kokernot knew what his friend Federico was up against. He quickly wrote back to tell Federico that he would feel privileged to have his sons work for him but could not hire Valentín because of the Baiza family's reputation.

Now all Federico had to do was break the news to Lico, Santos and Valentín.

The following morning, he got up early to ride out and check fences with his boys. It would give him the opportunity to talk to them all at one time.

He told them he couldn't afford for them to work on the ranch.

"But why Papá?" Lico asked.

"The law firm is making it difficult for us to run the ranch the way it should be run. There is not enough income to support all of our families. I cannot ask you and your families to go without."

"We need little, Papá," Santos replied.

"I have made inquiries with the Kokernots. They have work for you two. You can begin immediately."

"We cannot abandon you, Papá," Lico said.

"I knew that's how you would feel. I will be fine. The store and saddlery business in Santa Elena will support Severita and me. The ranch, at this point, can only support itself. You must go," Federico said.

Lico knew how deeply it hurt his father to make plans to operate the ranch without his sons.

Federico's dream had died, and his ranch was disappearing before his eyes, all because of the stupidity of two young boys who in an instant of insanity wiped out his life's work.

Lico, the least likely in the family to hurt a soul, was so angered that his burning wish was that he could raise the Coffmans from the dead and send them right back to hell where he was sure they had gone.

Miguel, for obvious reasons, was well aware of the family's financial crisis. He wanted to contribute. He proposed to Regina that he look for a job in town and work on the books evenings and weekends. Regina, aligned with her husband's sentiment, insisted on taking over full management of the Study Butte store and dismissed the storekeeper her father had hired when Jorge left. Severita cared for the children in her absence. The family was adapting, circling the wagons, and wondering, what more do we have to endure?

19

Federico Builds a New Ranch

Federico soon grew weary of working under Mead and Metcalfe's continual interference. In early 1927, he notified the law firm that he would sever their relationship and relocate to another part of the Big Bend. With an assist from his son, Felipe, Federico negotiated a lease with A. J. Compton for 1,640 acres about 40 miles downriver from Rancho Barras. It meant having to start over again. It also meant having to sell the store to put together the working captial for the new venture, but Federico preferred that to continuing to work under Metcalfe's management.

The new Rancho Barras was located in quite possibly the most picturesque part of the Big Bend. It was located twenty-six miles downriver from Castolón and 10 miles east of Elmo Johnson's ranch. Elmo and his wife, Ada, installed a trading post on their ranch and drew most of their trade from across the border. The Johnson Ranch at one time served as the local schoolhouse. In 1929, during the Escobar Rebellion, and after the ranch was raided by 30 *bandidos,* it also became an emergency landing field for the U.S. Army Air Corps.

Federico built a new ranch house on a promontory with spectacular views. The house's footprint measured some 1,500 square feet, consisting of seven rooms; three bedrooms, a sitting room, kitchen, study and dining room.

Federico had his men build a *kiva*, or beehive, style fireplace in the southeast corner of the living room. Outside, he built a porch that wrapped around the house. The *ramada* faced north in the direction of the road that brought visitors to the adobe, past the 20 x 20 rock house used for protection and weaponry in the event of an attack by hostile forces from either side of the border. To the east, below the promontory, was Federico, Jr. and María's adobe. Half the size of his father's home, with only one bedroom, it sat next to a tiny rock house used by the goat tender, Alfredo Avila, María's young brother.

María Avila de Villalba with baby Joseph

To the front of the house, above the rim of the river gorge, was a view of México and its landscape of rolling mesas covered in grassland and scrubland. Within a year, Pablo Baiza would build a little adobe house directly in front of Federico's home, half a mile or so from the riverbank on the Mexican side. Pablo would move his family to be closer to his good friend. Federico could be seen and heard on any given morning standing on the bluff overlooking the creek, enjoying his first cup of coffee and shouting greetings to his friend Pablo.

The Chisos Mountains, whose rocky peaks reach 7,825 feet, and the two distinctive peaks of lava that resembled mule ears, as they were called, sat to the rear of the home.

Beneath the promontory was the constant, pleasant sound of the Río Grande's churning waters. If a move had to be made, the location of the new ranch was the best of all choices.

Just as he had in Terlingua Abajo, Federico built an *arrastra*, or threshing circle. It was used to separate the wheat from the chaff by tying mules or cattle to a center post. They would trample the wheat stalks as they walked in a circle. He also installed commercial beehives for honey production. What was not used on the ranch was sold to Wayne Cartledge's and Howard Perry's La Harmonía store in Castolón. To Federico, it felt good to once again answer to no one except his own conscience.

In a year's time, he built his cattle herd and goats to respectable numbers and made his first shipment of cattle to his Chicago buyers. Federico made certain that the breeding bull sires he bought and the breeding stock would insure his continued ability to satisfy future cattle orders.

Together with his son, Jacobo, and other ranchers, Federico imported Red Poll cattle from England, hoping to raise a breed that would fatten in three years rather than the four to five it generally took. It was an expensive and ill-fated proposition, however. Shortly after the cattle arrived, the Villalba heifers were stolen.

Rumor had it that Det Walker had taken them. Predictably, as soon as the rumor reached Jacobo, he wanted to go after Walker. Federico quickly intervened, demanding that Jacobo let the authorities handle the theft. It took some convincing, but Jacobo finally agreed.

The Terlingua School and Howard Perry

In the 1920s, the economic situation in the Big Bend continued to improve along with the social and cultural life of the area. Four schoolteachers served the community's students. The majority of students were Mexican. Terlingua continued to grow. The school budget was nearly $1,000. All supplies were purchased from the Chisos store, giving Howard Perry a window into school expenditures. By 1930, the budget was almost $2,000, and Perry had the idea of consolidating the outlying schools and centralizing the Terlingua School District.

Once again, his motives probably had little to do with the welfare of the people of Terlingua or the quality of education but more to do with the prospect of lining his pockets with a new source of revenue, the school district's money. His idea was to construct a school building and have the district rent it from him as well as buy all of their supplies from his store.

Meetings were held. Perry's idea was not well received but not totally rejected. Probably feeling that he had the necessary political muscle to change the dissenters' minds, Perry began construction of a building. One of the requirements for a centralized district was a bridge across Terlingua Creek.

The school board eventually relented and gave verbal approval for the project. Robert Cartledge sent word to Perry of the board's action. Sensing victory, Perry immediately sent back word that he was doubling the rent. This incensed the community leaders of Study Butte who had strongly resisted Perry's move. They saw Perry's motivation for what it was and successfully convinced others to dismiss the Chisos Mining Company's agenda.

But this didn't deter Perry from completing construction of a school, which he named after himself. Instead of reciting the pledge of allegiance or a morning prayer, the children who attended the Perry-built school were required to sing, "Good morning, Mr. Perry" in tribute to their self-proclaimed benefactor.

Most of the school board members were from Terlingua and generally loyal to Perry. Even so, the board retained some semblance of dignity by resisting Perry's and Robert Cartledge's more outrageous maneuvers. One confrontation that led to Robert Cartledge's resignation from the board in protest was his wife's insistence that they segregate the children at the new Perry school. Mrs. Cartledge made it very clear to the teachers that they did not want their children mixing with the "Mexican kids."

Elizabeth Bledsoe, who taught both in Terlingua and Study Butte but preferred Study Butte, where she could avoid the Cartledges constant prying and interventions, organized the opposition and the majority of the board members sided with her.

Jacobo Dances with Danger

Jacobo was having his share of troubles with the Baiza brothers, mostly with Candelario. The shooting and wounding of Santos had created tension, but from a business standpoint not nearly as much as Candelario's activities.

The word from Jacobo's suppliers was that Candelario was asking for liquor in excess of Jacobo's orders, yet when he delivered the money, it would be for the amount of Jacobo's original order.

This meant Candelario was pocketing the difference. Jacobo brought this to Valentín's attention.

"*Manito*, it seems that your father is taking advantage of me," Jacobo confided to his best friend.

"I was sworn to secrecy," Valentín replied, ashamed and embarrassed at his father's larcenous behavior.

"I place no fault with you. Your father is a hard man. I know the pressure he can put on you. What should I do?" Jacobo asked.

"You must tell him you know."

"Confronting your father will only incite him. I know he will take it out on you," Jacobo said. "I don't want that to happen. I'll tell you what I will do. I will tell my suppliers to deliver the product directly to the ranch. That way I can keep count on what goes out. What do you think?"

Valentín grinned broadly. "As I've said many times before, you are wise beyond your years."

It was in Jacobo's nature to work his bootlegging business in spite of his earlier troubles with the law. His nature was to court danger.

Jacobo Charged with Murder

On January 29, 1930, Federico received a visit from a frightened and disheveled Valentín Baiza.

"My father and my uncle killed Nacho and Isidro García," Valentín told Federico.

Federico knew the Garcia brothers were cousins to the Baizas and were married to the Holguin sisters, which was about all he knew of them. His boys didn't run in their circle.

"*¿Qué pasó?*"

"We were playing cards. Nacho accused me of cheating. The next thing I know, he pulls a knife and cuts me," said Valentín, opening his shirt to show Federico a bloody wrapping covering his ribs.

"I told her not too, but Tía Noné insisted on sending word to my father and my uncle. The cut isn't that deep. The Garcías apologized to me. They said they would stay and apologize to my father. When my father arrived he was angry and yelling.

"Nacho got mouthy and my father took his rifle out of the sleeve on his saddle and shot him. Isidro ran for the river. My Papá chased him and shot him in the back as he reached the reeds along the water."

It suddenly occurred to Federico that Jacobo had visited him earlier in the day and talked about going to play cards at Pablo's house.

"Where was Jacobo when all of this happened?"

"I haven't seen him all day," Valentín said.

"He was here earlier. He said he was going to your place to play cards," Federico said.

"He never showed. He must have gone to his ranch," Valentín said, with a puzzled look on his face.

"Are you sure they're dead?

"They're dead alright. Tío and Papá tied their feet with a rope and drug them around for a while and then to someone's goat pen away from the house and left them there."

"Do the authorities know yet?"

"Not yet," Valentín said.

"Will your family never learn?" Federico said in frustration.

Candelario Baiza was a bloody-minded killer, Federico thought to himself. *These were two more lives he could notch on his gun.*

"Get back home. The Garcías will certainly come gunning for you."

Valentín did not heed Federico's instructions. Instead he went directly to Jacobo's house where he was greeted by his friend. Valentín repeated the story.

"*Cálmate manito.* Where are your dad and uncle now?"

"They're in México."

"Who else was at the card game?" Jacobo asked.

"My cousins, Pablo and Adolfo," he said.

"Did they have anything to do with the shootings?"

"No."

"Did you?"

"No."

Valentín's answers seemed tentative.

"Don't lie to me," Jacobo demanded.

Valentín shook his head in shame, disgust and fear.

"We kicked the boys and spit on them after they'd been killed, but we had nothing to do with the shootings."

Jacobo thought back to the day he shot the Coffmans and the chaos following the incident. He knew all hell would break loose. This time there was a witness. Dragging the bodies away from the house was not going to keep the law from coming after them.

Little did Jacobo know that his friendship with Valentín would also drag him into the fray. Because the García brothers were U.S. born, arrest warrants were issued by the Brewster County Sheriff for Candelario, Pablo, Pablo Jr., Adolfo and Jacobo and all were indicted for the murders of the Garcías. Only Pablo Sr. and Adolfo were arrested. Fearing that no one would believe that he had nothing to do with the killings, Jacobo stayed at his ranch in México. The others eluded the authorities and were never apprehended.

Noné contacted and hired Mead & Metcalfe, as Federico had seven years earlier. She gave the law firm a $600 retainer and signed over 100 head of cattle and their lease rights to two large parcels of grazing land. The case was brought to trial on September 3, 1930.

Though witnesses attested to Baiza's notorious reputation, the prosecution's case hinged on the testimony of a young man, Alfredo Avila, the son of Rosendo, and younger brother of María, Lico's wife.

Avila had left his goats and crossed the Río Grande onto the Baiza ranch upon hearing gunshots. Unfortunately, he arrived in time to see Candelario and Pablo rope and drag the boys' bodies. Frightened out of his mind, Alfredo managed to sneak back to the Villalba ranch unseen. He hurried to tell his sister who immediately recruited a *vaquero* to take him to Terlingua to tell the Justice of the Peace. Her father, Rosendo and the rest of the men were away on a cattle drive.

Afraid for her brother's life, María insisted that he be placed in protective custody after apprising Cartledge of the killings. Cartledge agreed. For the next nine months, Alfredo's home was a 10 x 10-foot cell in the Brewster County jail in Alpine.

The trial was a fiasco. The prosecution's star witness was literally frightened beyond words by the presence of the Baiza clan, especially Noné. When he was finally called to the witness stand, Alfredo was so nervous that he asked the judge for permission to stand through his testimony, presumably to be in a better position to run in the event one of the Baizas came after him. Each time the prosecutor asked him a question, curiously and effectively, Noné Baiza stood up at the back of the courtroom and stared ominously at young Avila.

Each time the judge would admonish her and tell her to sit down. This happened several times until the judge finally threatened to hold Noné in contempt and jail her if she stood up one more time.

By that time, the damage had been done. The young man's testimony had been rendered ineffective by her brazen behavior. The jury deliberated five minutes and delivered a not guilty verdict. All charges against everyone who had been indicted were dropped.

Damaged Reputations

The lives of Jacobo and Federico were once again in turmoil. Jacobo had been implicated in two murders he had nothing to do with. The Baiza family was now at odds with the Avilas and the Villalbas. People of Mexican descent had to combat Anglo prejudices. Now they were fighting among themselves. Predictably and sadly, Jacobo's relationship with Valentín soured. His partnership with Candelario and Pablo ended, as did his bootlegging business.

The second murder charge had cost Jacobo a friendship, a great deal of money and the reputation he'd worked so hard to improve following the Coffman shootings.

Federico and his son Jacobo branding a calf

Jacobo's U.S. bootlegging and business dealings were at a stand-still for the nine months it took for the Baizas to be tried for the García killings and for the charges against him to be dropped.

Federico couldn't do much of anything on his son's behalf for fear that he would draw unwanted attention to the family business. Federico had missed two consignment shipments of cattle. Relationships with the buyers out of Chicago became strained. Had it not been for Federico's previous good will and good word, buyers would have walked away. Both father and son now had to deal with repairing their businesses, and, once again, their reputation.

Even though Jacobo was vindicated, from that point on he was known as *el proscrito*, the prohibited one, the outlaw.

In Search of a New Home

Regina wanted to return from El Paso the minute she read the letter from Severita telling her of Jacobo's plight. Federico told her not to come. Once again, the area had become hostile to the Villalbas, only this time it hadn't been the Anglo citizenry that was up in arms. It was the Baizas, Garcías, and their kin.

Had it not been for the children, Regina would have disregarded her father's advice. She wanted to be closer to home. She convinced Miguel to take her and the children to his family's ranch near Ciudad Acuña across from Del Río on the U.S. side, where they stayed for a few months. What had started out as a vacation slowly began to feel like a life of exile.

Regina and Miguel

Regina now had four children. Their school-aged children were home-schooled. In 1930, Miguel and Regina made plans to travel to México for a vacation while they decided what to do next. After visiting Federico at the ranch, Regina, Miguel and the children piled into the *Fordingo* and set off for Villa Unión to visit Miguel's parents.

"We'll write as soon as we arrive, Papá," Regina shouted, trying to get Tony and Herminia to stop crying. They wanted nothing to do with leaving *"Abuelito" y "Abuelita"*, Grandpa and Grandma.

Herminia was especially attached to her *Abuelita*. She would follow Severita everywhere as she did her daily chores.

"Mi mosquita, me sigues por todas partes, my little fly, you follow me everywhere," Severita would say.

"Vayan con Dios," Severita wished the group, lifting the corner of her apron to dab her eyes. Severita had entered fully into the family's hearts.

Federico had grown fond of having children at the ranch again. His grandchildren had become a big part of the family unit.

Lico and Santos had both moved to Alpine to be closer to work. Federico didn't get to see their children unless he made a trip to Alpine, which was infrequently, or when they came to Terlingua for supplies. Federico had accounts for both of them at the Chisos Store and at La Harmonía. He would always pay their tabs if they couldn't. It was his way of making certain they were well cared for, a small price to pay for his peace of mind.

20

A Woman in the Wilderness

Jacobo had to make up for lost time. Cattle had been consigned just before the García murders and had to be moved to the rail-head by the end of September. He hired extra drovers and worked day and night to get this accomplished. Federico suggested moving the consigned cattle with unweaned calves to Rancho Barras where he and his *vaqueros* would lend a hand in the branding.

"Papá, the Baiza's antics have cost me big," Jacobo told his father. "I should never have given them my confidence."

Federico saw the mixture of frustration and resentment in his son's face. He felt responsible for his son's predicament.

"*Mi hijo*, Pablo has been my friend for many years. Over the years he has done some foolish things, but unless it endangered my family, I would turn a blind eye.

"That was wrong of me. I set an example. You merely followed it. I should have heeded the warning signs and taught you to do the same. Instead, I chose to remain friends with Pablo. You chose to do business with Candelario. We entered a pit of vipers. We were foolish to think we could walk among them and not be bitten."

"I don't blame you, Papá. I made my own choices. I must live with their consequences. *¿Tienes hambre*, are you hungry?" Jacobo said, changing the subject.

"Dying of hunger," Federico joked.

"Severita gave me some burritos before we left. I've got them in the saddlebag."

"What are we waiting for?"

After lunch the men mounted their horses and set out to round up more calves for branding. As they were riding, Jacobo noticed black dots in the distance descending from the sky.

"*Mira, Papá*, looks like we might have lost some stock," Jacobo said, pointing in the direction of the vultures.

"Let's go see," Federico said, wasting no time as he spurred his horse.

The men rode towards the scavengers at full gallop. They came into heavy, almost impassable scrub brush and were surprised to see a lean-to, newly constructed.

"What's this?" Federico asked.

As they approached the shelter, they could hear a combination of children crying and what sounded like a woman's groans. They dismounted and announced themselves. When no one came to greet them, they poked their heads around the stack of mesquite branches. The smell was horrendous. A woman whose dress was soaked in blood lay on a blanket on the dirt. A girl who appeared to be around seven and her smaller brother knelt, crying beside their mother.

"Mom is very ill," the little girl said.

Federico guessed it might be female problems, judging from the location of the blood. Jacobo knelt beside the woman who was half-conscious.

"What is wrong, *señora?*" he asked.

"Miscarriage, please help me," the woman pleaded.

According to the children, they were traveling from México to Terlingua for the first time and became lost. When their mother began feeling ill and started bleeding, their father built the lean-to and went for help. It had been a day and a night. There was little water and no food.

Federico stood and took Jacobo by the arm.

"Let's go get the wagon."

"We'll never get it here through all that scrub brush, Papá," Jacobo said.

"That's what *machetes* are for, *mi hijo*."

Federico and Jacobo rode hard and fast to the ranch. While Jacobo readied the wagon, Federico told Severita what they had happened on. Severita grabbed some sheets, blankets, and alcohol and had Federico fill a container of water and all three set off to aid the woman. Thankfully, when they arrived the woman was still alive. Severita shooed the men outside while she attended to the woman. After she called them back in, they loaded the woman and the children on the wagon and drove them back to the ranch. Dr. Wilson was waiting at Rancho Barras when they returned.

Federico sent his *vaquero*, cook and tracker, "*El Negro Mogi*," to find the husband. Mogi, a black Seminole Indian, was once in the employ of the U.S. Army as an Indian scout. The Black Seminoles were descendants of escaped slaves that fled to Florida. They lived and married among the Seminole. In the late 1830s and early 1840s, the Seminoles were moved to Oklahoma, then called "Indian Territory."

One band of Seminoles and a band of Black Seminoles moved to México, because of persecution by slave hunters and Creek Indians. Mogi came to the Big Bend and was recruited by the military. He served in Fort Davis until he was nearly killed by an Apache warrior.

When he was granted a release from the military, having heard that Federico was looking for a *vaquero*, Mogi wandered onto

Rancho Barras where he was immediately hired. In addition to his ranch duties, he was responsible for the chuck wagon on cattle drives.

Mogi searched for three days before he found a wagon and a dead horse, but no husband. There were many things that could have happened to the man and none were pleasant to think of.

Once the woman regained her strength and her senses, Federico told her about the wagon and horse. She quietly gathered her children and the few belongings Jacobo had retrieved from the shanty. She was taken to Santa Elena, where Federico had arranged for her to work for a family friend.

Regina's Homesick

Regina was ready to return to Rancho Barras. Miguel, however, had been communicating with his family in Ocampo two hundred miles to the south. Knowing that their cousin had political aspirations, they wrote him of the upcoming municipal elections, suggesting that he come down and try his hand at running for the *ayuntamiento*, the municipal council. Politics intrigued and enticed Miguel. The challenge was to convince his wife to move deeper into México, a notion she adamantly resisted.

"*Mi amor*, my cousins want me to run for the municipal council," Miguel announced to his wife.

"*Ni Dios lo quiera*, may God not want this," Regina said in astonishment and anger. "I want to go home."

"We can go and visit for a short time, but I feel a civic duty to travel to Ocampo," Miguel said.

"What you feel is a need to have me away from my family where you don't feel threatened," Regina countered.

In truth, Miguel did feel intimidated by the strength and bond of the Villalba family, not to mention the overwhelming and commanding influence of Federico. It was virtually impossible for Miguel to have any control over Regina and his children when they were anywhere near her father. Perhaps she was right. Whatever his motivation, he had no desire to return to live in Terlingua. With promises of a beautiful house in Ocampo, servants and frequent visits to the ranch, Regina relented and agreed to the move.

Jorge Villalba with trophy

"*Pero mira*, but look, Miguel," she began, pointing her finger at him, "if what you promise doesn't happen, I am going home—with or without you. *¿Comprendes?*"

"*Comprendo*," Miguel said.

Regina came to visit for her father's birthday the following November. During her visit, Federico complained to her of losing cattle to black bears. "The bears are fattening up on mesquite beans and too many of my cattle before winter hibernation sets in."

"I would love to take a bear rug back to Ocampo," Regina said.

In years past, she would have joined the bear hunt but with a husband and four children, Miguel reminded her that participation was out of the question.

The arrival of 1931 was accompanied by the marriage of Santos to Isidora Baiza. They married in a small civil ceremony in Terlingua. Santos installed Isidora in the rock house at Rancho Barras.

Santos' plans were to leave the Kokernot ranch and return to a small spread he and Lico had bought not far from Rancho Barras. They'd bought a few cattle and were breeding the stock with plans on ranching on their own. Dividing their time between Alpine and their ranch wasn't easy, but it was rewarding and hopeful.

"Jacobo said he's got some stud bulls he can sell us," Santos said.

Lico smiled. "We'll buy them. Come spring, our bulls will have their way. They will be happy. We will be happy."

Santos' and Isidora's nuptials

Jacobo's Temper
Leads to Danger

In November, 1931, Federico celebrated his 73rd birthday by taking Severita to Big Spring to visit Jorge, who now had six children. It was hard to remember a time when Golla wasn't pregnant.

Jacobo had come the day before and given him a set of matched .45 revolvers with pearl handles. Federico had mentioned in passing how he admired the pair Jacobo had a Mexican gunsmith make for him the year before. He was not surprised to see that his remark had been interpreted as a request. It was Jacobo's way.

What Federico didn't know was that his son's guns had also been admired by Det Walker years back at a bar in Castolón. On that night, Jacobo kept a vigilant eye on Walker. He was prepared to draw his gun at any sudden movement from the man.

Egged on by his friends and fortified by sotol, Det walked over.

Jacobo smiled curiously at his friend Tiburcio García as Walker approached him.

"*Este pendejo tiene cojones,*" Jacobo said.

"What'd you say, Mexican?" Walker asked.

"I wasn't talking to you, but if you must know, I said you've got balls coming over here."

"I wanna buy them guns," Walker announced, disregarding Jacobo's remark.

"Even if they were for sale, I sure as hell wouldn't sell them to you," Jacobo said.

"They're mighty fine looking pistols," Walker said.

"Thank you, now why don't you get your ass back to your friends and let me drink in peace."

"How about a shootin' contest? I'll put up 20 head of cattle. You put up them guns."

"I don't think so," Jacobo said. There wasn't a man in the Big Bend that was faster or more accurate than Jacobo. He didn't need any cattle, and he sure as hell didn't need any trouble. He knew Walker would lose, and what then?

"Maybe you're not as good as they say you are," Walker said, needling Jacobo.

Jacobo looked down to the floor and then over to Tiburcio. Walker's attitude brought up the emotions he'd felt during their very first encounter.

"Let's just see who can hit a silver dollar at 25 paces," Jacobo said. "That's fine," Walker agreed.

The men left the building constructed of *lajitas,* or flagstone, and walked towards a corral behind the bar. Nearly all of the bar patrons followed behind.

"I'll go first," Jacobo announced. He gave Tiburcio a silver dollar and asked him to step off twenty-five paces. Tiburcio did as he was told.

"Hold it up!" Jacobo yelled.

Without hesitation, Tiburcio stretched his arm upward as far as it could go and held the coin between the tips of his fingers.

"*Listo,* ready?" Jacobo yelled.

"*Listo.*"

"Jacobo drew his gun and with little hesitation fired and hit the silver dollar dead center, shooting it out of his friend's hand. Tiburcio shook his hand and rubbed his fingertips. He walked back to collect the silver dollar. He carried the coin towards the two men and the large crowd that had followed them out of the bar. He raised his hand and the silver dollar for inspection.

Astounded at Jacobo's marksmanship, Walker said nervously,

"You sure as hell don't expect me to shoot a dollar out of your man's hand, do you, Mexican?"

There was a corral post about two feet this side of where Tiburcio had stood.

"Put it on one of the posts," Jacobo suggested.

Walker walked down to the post and dug the edge of the coin into one of the cracks of the soft weathered lumber. He walked back, drew his weapon, squinted and took careful aim.

The echo of the gun's blast was nearly drowned out by the cheers of the crowd. For an instant, Walker thought the men were cheering for him. He focused his eyes on the post and saw the coin was still sitting securely in the distance. He had missed. More cheers went up for Jacobo.

Angry and humiliated, Walker holstered his gun and turned to Jacobo.

"Looks like you win. I'll have the cattle for you next week. You can come and get them."

"I don't think so. Take them to my father's ranch," Jacobo replied.

The embarrassment in Walker's eyes was visible to all. He left without agreeing to Jacobo's demand. Walker never delivered the cattle. Jacobo didn't expect he would, and he didn't really care.

'I'm Old, Not Dead'

Regina sent birthday wishes to her father by telegram. She was being the dutiful, albeit reluctant, political wife in Ocampo. The political machinery had taken a liking to Miguel. In fact, he was being encouraged to run for the Mexican senate, a circumstance that did not set well with Regina. Her husband's political success was bittersweet. It seemed the harder she pushed her husband to return to the U.S., the more alluring it became for him to stay.

Jorge and his family greeted Federico and Severita warmly. Federico was in his element when family surrounded him. All but the infant Golla was carrying clung to Federico as he walked into Jorge's home.

"How was your trip, Papá?" Jorge asked.

"These trips seem longer as I grow older. I am tired."

"You need to slow down *viejo*, old man. Jacobo writes me of you insisting on helping brand and inoculate his herd," Jorge said.

"He won't listen to you," Severita injected. "He's too stubborn."

Federico hugged the two grandchildren sitting on his lap before responding to his wife.

"As long as I have strength in my body, I will work. *¡Estoy viejo, no muerto,* I'm old, not dead!" Federico said.

21

Jacobo's Caught in a Trap

Jacobo and his *vaqueros* were hard at work getting the cattle ready for winter. His father had returned from his trip to Big Spring. He was anxious to know how the trip had gone and made time to go see him and Severita. When he arrived, he found that Severita's sister, Juliana, and her husband, Francisco Briceño, were visiting from Marathon.

"Another hand to help with the chores," Jacobo joked with Tío Pancho.

"*Seguro qué si,*" Francisco replied.

Juliana laughed. "*Está viejo ya no sopla,* this old man can't whistle a tune and you want him to help you?"

Francisco shook his head half amused, half embarrassed.

"Jacobo, when are you going to come up to Marathon to visit us?" Francisco asked, changing the subject.

"Grief doesn't last one hundred years," Jacobo answered, referring to the stigma of being considered an outlaw.

"When things cool down, Tio," he said.

Severita prepared a wonderful meal for her visitors. After dinner, Federico and the men retired to the study for drinks. It grew late. After a few too many drinks and stories, Jacobo decided to spend the night. He slept on the veranda with his guns and rifle

Jacobo (far right), Tiburcio in middle, and unidentified friend on the left

next to him. He did not feel safe anywhere outside of his ranch in Santa Elena.

Severita went to the veranda with a cup of coffee for Jacobo the next morning. He wasn't there. She walked across the courtyard to the stables thinking he might be there. His horse was gone. It was uncharacteristic of him to leave without announcing his departure. She went back to the house to find her visitors and Federico gathered at the kitchen table.

"Where were you, my love?" Federico asked.

"I went to give your son some coffee and found that he was gone," she answered.

"He must have had something urgent to get back to."

Just then, the group heard a horse ride up and the bleating of a goat. Jacobo came in through the kitchen door by way of the ramada.

"I brought you a kid goat you could take home with you," he said with a smile. "Fatten it up for my trip to visit you."

Federico smiled at his son's charitable nature.

"Really?" Juliana beamed.

Jacobo had thought about the excuse he'd make to Severita's brother-in-law the day before about not traveling to Marathon. He'd come to the conclusion that he would no longer be held captive by his reputation.

"Write me when you're ready to make me the *birria* (goat stew) that you're famous for," Jacobo replied with a wink.

"*Hecho*, done," Francisco said straight away.

"Papá, I have to go."

"Please stay for breakfast," Severita begged.

"I can't. Carmelita is probably furious that I stayed the night."

Jacobo looked over at his stepmother's sister.

"Tía Juliana, Tío Pancho, if God allows, I will see you in Marathon soon," he said, kissing his father, stepmother and Juliana on the cheek.

"Go with God, my son," Federico said as his son left in haste.

The ride along the riverbank to Castolón took about one hour. He was sure Carmelita would be waiting for him at home with her *palote*, rolling pin. He crossed the Río Grande at a place that was well traveled by the *zacateros* who brought chino grass picked from the Chihuahan Mountains across the river to sell to ranchers who used it as a substitute for hay and oats in the winter months.

As expected, Carmelita was furious.

"*¿Te emborrachaste*, you got drunk didn't you? "

"Aren't you happy to see me?" Jacobo asked, reaching out to hug her.

Carmelita angrily pushed Jacobo's arms aside.

"*¡Quítate de aquí*, get away from me!"

"If you don't calm down, I'm leaving," Jacobo warned.

She found Jacobo's ultimatum infuriating.

"Go if you want." Anger dripped from her words.

Jacobo knew Carmelita was beyond reason. It would be better to go somewhere and let her calm down. He decided to go back to Barras.

He hoisted himself onto his horse and looked into the doorway to see if Carmelita might motion for him to come back. She didn't. Instead she retreated to their bedroom perhaps more disappointed than angry because she wasn't able to tell Jacobo that she was with child, something she'd planned to disclose the previous night during the romantic dinner she'd prepared.

As Jacobo approached Rancho Barras, he decided instead to cross into México and visit with the Baizas. The afternoon started out innocently enough. Carlos and Adolfo were playing dominoes on the porch when Jacobo rode up.

"What brings you in our way?" Carlos asked.

"Carmelita is very angry with me because I stayed at Barras last night," he said.

"Come play a game with us!" Carlos shouted. "It will take your mind off your troubles."

The boys had been playing and drinking for an hour or so when a *vaquero* by the name of Norberto de la Paz from the neighboring ranch showed up with a bottle of sotol.

"Got room for another player?" he asked.

"Sure!" the boys yelled. Norberto would come over from time to time. Jacobo had met him once or twice. The afternoon slid into more conversation and sotol than domino playing. It wasn't long before the second bottle was nearly empty.

"I hear Walker's looking for Jacobo," de la Paz announced out of the blue. "He's telling everyone Jacobo is cowardly for not having gone to collect the cattle he stole from him." He continued, not daring to face Jacobo, fearing the young Villalba would become physical.

Jacobo looked over at the man with a steely glare.

"And who told you this?" he asked.

No longer able to avoid facing Jacobo, de la Paz answered, "I don't remember. I just heard it around town."

Carlos and Adolfo looked first at de la Paz and then at Jacobo. They could see de la Paz's words riled their friend.

"Don't get any ideas, Cobito," Carlos warned.

"Do you two think I'm afraid of him?" Jacobo asked, annoyed at Carlos's warning.

Suddenly, Carlos became wary of de la Paz. He looked at Jacobo in frustration then cast an angry glance towards de la Paz.

"What business is it of yours that Walker is talking about our friend?" he asked. The man's presence and purpose suddenly became very suspicious.

"Look, man, I didn't mean anything by it. I just thought Jacobo would want to know."

Jacobo stood. He felt for his guns and started towards his horse. He hated rustlers, and he hated cowards even more. He was tired of waiting for the law to do something.

"¿Cobito, estás loco?" Carlos shouted.

Jacobo said nothing and continued towards his horse. Before

Carlos or Adolfo were able to intercept him, he was on his horse, presumably headed to the Talley ranch where he was most likely to find Walker.

Carlos ran and leaped from the porch onto his saddle, simultaneously reaching for his lariat. He swung the loop over his head and threw it towards his friend just as Jacobo was about to spur his horse into a gallop. The rope found its intended quarry, cinching securely around Jacobo's chest and pulling him off of his horse. Stunned by the fall, Jacobo lay on his back, hurting and laughing at what had just happened. The two brothers rushed over to help Jacobo up.

"Don't go," Carlos implored.

"Don't worry—I won't go."

When the trio looked back towards the house, de la Paz was gone.

Carlos slapped at the dust on his friends back.

"Go to your father's place and sober up," he pleaded.

Jacobo smiled at his friends.

"I'll go. Don't worry, I'll be alright."

Jacobo had no intention of going home. He merely wanted to draw the Baizas off the scent. He would go find Walker and settle it once and for all. Jacobo rode in the direction of his father's ranch for as long as he was within sight of the boys. Out of their view, he turned in the direction of the Talley ranch.

The following is what the Villalba family believes happened based on the physical evidence at the scene and the circumstantial evidence of the event. The official investigation into the murder was unable to gather sufficient evidence to determine who committed the murder, although most contemporary observers believed the Walker family played a role.

Jacobo arrived at the river crossing near Johnson "Jonce" Walker's Talley Ranch where he was told Det would be.

Jacobo crossed the river towards the ranch with his mind still clouded by the sotol. Perhaps if he had been sober he would not have been so unsuspecting. He turned in the direction of the ranch house. He reached the front and immediately announced his purpose. "Det, I've come for my cattle."

"A voice from inside answered back. "Jake, go home. We don't have your cattle."

The voice wasn't Dets. Det's brother, Otto was also in the house.

"Otto, send your coward brother out to face me," Jacobo yelled.

Det finally spoke, "I ain't comin' out Mexican. Go home!"

Jacobo smiled. *The sonofabitch is here,* he thought to himself. *I'll wait him out.* Jacobo waited a few more minutes before deciding to remain at the river's edge where, because of the slope, he couldn't be seen from the house. Without saying any more, he turned his horse around to find himself a place to hide. Det had to come out sooner or later.

Suddenly a shot rang out. Jacobo felt the burning of a bullet pierce his back. He reached for his guns but before he could retrieve them or turn to see who had shot him, a second, and then a third shot hit him, one in each arm. The next shot hit him at the base of the neck, causing his upper torso to lurch forward onto his saddle horn. The sound of rapid gunfire and the erratic movement of the rider caused the horse to veer, spilling Jacobo's lifeless body to the ground but not before nine shots had found their mark. One man couldn't have fired all the shots.

De la Paz had done his job. He drew Jacobo to the web that Det Walker had spun where he could inject his poison through the venomous barrel of his .30-30. The large caliber bullets blew away most of Jacobo's chest.

Walker had avenged the humiliation he'd suffered at the hands of Jacobo. All he needed was his hatred for the man to convince himself that killing the "outlaw" Jacobo Villalba would be considered an act of heroism. He walked over to Jacobo's body and dug the heel of his boot into Jacobo's back to make doubly certain he was dead. Jacobo's horse backed away slowly while the strange men inspected his master who lay motionless on the ground. Drawn to the gleam of the pearl handled revolvers, Walker slipped them out of their holsters, deciding to take them as his trophy. He walked away with his booty, proud of what he had just done.

As Walker and the other man left, Jacobo's horse returned to nudge his master to wake him as it had done so many times during cattle drives. The horse circled the body. Every so often it would push and sniff to see if the body moved. Finally, when the body grew cold, the horse set out to Rancho Barras without its rider.

Grim News

Francisco and Juliana had agreed to stay an extra day. Severita and her sister were in the kitchen busily preparing for the evening meal when she heard Federico yell for her. She rushed towards her husband's voice as she wiped the biscuit dough off of her hands. She saw Jacobo's horse trotting towards Federico who had run to the middle of the courtyard to inspect the animal. Federico saw the dried blood on the horse's flank and on the saddle. The second he saw the horse, he knew his son was dead. He looked down and pressed his head to the saddle as he rubbed his fingertips across his eyes.

"Let us go and find my son," Federico said, fighting back his emotions.

"Severita, get word to Sheriff Townsend. Tell them to meet us here at the ranch."

Federico called on El Negro Mogi to track Jacobo's horse. They found Jacobo's body at the Talley place. He knew immediately Det Walker had finally taken his revenge. He took his son's body to Barras but not before checking the Walker house and finding it empty. God knows what would have happened had any of the Walker men been home.

Hours later, Townsend showed up after asking around for Federico. The entire town soon knew what had happened and who had killed Jacobo.

"What happened, old friend?" the sheriff asked.

"They killed my son," Federico said.

"Do you know who?"

"*El cabrón*, the sonofabitch Det Walker," Federico answered. There was an old saying that rang so true. *El valiente vive hasta que el cobarde quiera*, the brave one lives only as long as the coward wants.

Federico thought back to the many conversations he'd had with Townsend about his son. The sheriff had always voiced concern for Jacobo's welfare. He would say, "There are many men who'd like nothing more than to notch their guns with your son's life."

Federico told Sheriff Townsend that his son's pearl handled revolvers were missing when they found his body. "Tell Walker I want them back."

The sheriff knew that Federico's chances of seeing the guns again were slim and none. He wouldn't hear that from him.

"I'll see what I can do, old friend."

There was still some light left in the sky. Townsend quietly left for Boquillas where he'd been told the Walkers were hiding out.

Federico sent a *vaquero* to tell Carmelita of Jacobo's death. She was accompanied back to the ranch where they were preparing Jacobo's body for vigil. She kissed Jacobo for the last time. Carmelita did not tell Federico that she was carrying Jacobo's child. No Villalba would ever know.

Jacobo was Severita's favorite. She had always feared he would die by another man's hand. Her worst fears had been realized.

"Ay Cobito, Cobito. What happened, my son?" Severita wailed as she washed the blood from Jacobo's body. Her body shook as she sobbed loudly and uncontrollably.

Juliana put her arm around her sister to console her.

"Sister, please don't cry so much, you're going to become ill,"

"Juliana, I could not have loved this child any more if he'd been my own."

She had known Jacobo almost all of his life. Her friendship with María dated back to about the time Santos was born, when Jacobo was four. She remembered that during catechism, he was the most inquisitive about the existence of God. He never questioned God's presence. He just always wanted to know how he could tell God was around.

Severita told him that when he felt a breeze against his face it was God's whisper that He loved him and it was His assurance that He would always be with him. Even as an adult, she sometimes saw Jacobo close his eyes and smile when he felt a breeze at his face. Jacobo looked peaceful. With hands shaking, she reached down and pulled the sheet over Jacobo's face. She thought at that moment that when he died it was in God's embrace. It was her only consolation.

Where is Justice?

Candelario Baiza became enraged at the news of Jacobo's death. He immediately rode to his brother, Pablo's house to enlist his help in avenging Jacobo's death. Though Candelario showed little or no affection for Jacobo in life, he did respect the man and felt some affinity for the family. After all, his niece Isidora was married to a Villalba.

"Brother let us go and kill Walker and his family. They're a pack of damned animals," he said.

Pablo was just as incensed as his older brother but not quite as crazy.

Jacobo Villalba tiendido (lying in state)
Federico and Severita in background on left side of photo

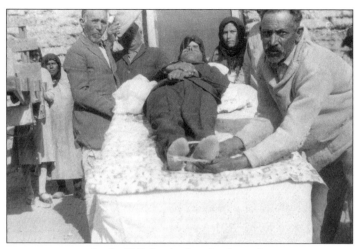

Jacobo Villalba displayed at his wake

"As much as I would like to take revenge, it makes little sense," Pablo said. What good would we do our families if we were to do as you wish? We would start a war. There would be much bloodshed. This is one that we need to think out, big brother. If we kill them, they cannot know it was us."

"I don't care if they know it was me. They can follow me to hell if they want," Candelario bellowed.

"*Hermano*, I've done your bidding before and it nearly cost my son and me our freedom and possibly our lives. Not this time. If you do this, you do it alone."

Candelario stormed out of the house and rode away. He had to admit that some of what his brother said made sense. He knew that if he acted alone he would never be caught, but every Mexican in town would pay for his sins. He would wait, but not for long. Det Walker had to die.

Severita and Juliana bathed Jacobo's body, preparing him for his final journey. Sheriff Townsend returned with a Texas Ranger and after an examination by the two, Jacobo was prepared for viewing and taken to the home of Santiago García in Terlingua where people could pay their respects.

Regina received word by telegram that her brother had been shot and killed. Miguel was out of town on a buying trip for the store he had opened in Ocampo. She packed her and the children's things into her car and left instructions with the housekeeper to tell him what had happened and to join her in Terlingua when he returned. Regina had never driven in the interior of México unaccompanied. She took her pistol with her, just in case.

As the Villalbas mourned Jacobo's death, Det and his accomplice hid behind the badge of the Texas Ranger in Boquillas. Jonce Walker had provided his son with the alibi he needed to convince the Texas Ranger and the sheriff that Jacobo had drawn first and that they were merely defending themselves.

It didn't matter that Jacobo had been shot in the back or that his weapons were missing. All that mattered was that he was Mexican, and he was trespassing. His son Jorge was accused of murdering an Anglo and even though it was clearly self-defense, he was prosecuted. His son Jacobo was shot in the back—and the killers are not even charged. Where was the justice?

Sheriff Townsend could not blame his old friend for his bitterness. As strong as he felt that a more thorough investigation should have taken place, political pressures being what they were, it wouldn't do for an Anglo to be convicted of killing a Mexican.

Two weeks after Jacobo's death, most likely to throw the Villalbas and the Baizas off his scent, Walker recanted his confession claiming that Joe Graham Barnett had killed Jacobo. Alpine resident and former Texas Ranger, Barnett was a lighting fast gun, and according to Walker, had been hired to protect his family from "Mexican bad man", Jacobo. Conveniently, this assertion came only after Barnett himself had been shot and killed by Upton County Sheriff William C. Fowler in neighboring Rankin over a debt supposedly owed by Fowler. Months back, Barnett had sold Sheriff Fowler a Thompson sub-machine gun, allowing him to take the gun with the understanding that he would pay for it later. As of December 6, 1931, Fowler had yet to pay Barnett for the gun. On that day, Barnett and friends, Rhome Shiveley and Tony Hess, set out in his car to collect his money or his gun.

Having heard Barnett was in town and looking for him, Fowler intercepted him at a gas station in town. Words were exchanged, and according to Fowler, Barnett drew his weapon first. Fowler fired off seven shots with one quick squeeze of the sub-machine gun's trigger instantly killing Barnett.

Barnett's friend, Tony Hess, described the incident differently. According to Hess, Fowler drove past the station and then turned around stopping his car about twenty paces from Barnett's. He lowered his window, ordered Hess to "stand aside" as he stuck the muzzle out of the window and began firing. When questioned about what Hess had said, all Fowler would say was that he "had to do it". Fowler was charged with murder, tried at Sonora on a change of venue. He was finally acquitted.

In Brewster County, the Grand Jury elected not to indict Walker, for Jacobo's murder. When Walker was told that he would not be prosecuted for Jacobo's death, he left the Big Bend for Durango, Colorado, probably because he feared that if he stuck around, a Villalba or someone else might take revenge. Little did he know that Candelario Baiza would most likely have been his executioner.

22

Here I Live
and Here I Die

In the month following Jacobo's murder, Federico's children all came for the Christmas holidays with grandchildren in tow. Miguel had returned for Jacobo's funeral but because of political and business affairs could not stay long. Regina refused to return to Ocampo with him. She and the children remained. Miguel succeeded in convincing his wife to return with him later in the year just before the arrival of fall. It would have been imprudent to travel any later because of the frigid cold of the high desert, and it would be a grueling trip for their four-month old daughter, Socorro.

With Jacobo's death still fresh on everyone's mind, the excitement and innocence of the Villalba and Esquivel grandchildren helped dull the pain of Jacobo's absence.

Felipe was especially concerned about his father's health. Even with his grandchildren around, Federico could not mask the toll Jacobo's murder had taken on his physical health.

"Papá, come and live with me," Felipe pleaded."

"And what will I do?" Federico replied.

"Rest Papá—something you earned and deserve."

"*Mi hijo*, my life is here."

"Papá, you and the family are in danger here. Perhaps you should consider returning to México."

There was an uncomfortable moment of silence before either spoke.

"I will give it some thought," Federico said, hoping to appease his son.

"And what of Jacobo's business affairs?" Felipe asked, moving to another subject he felt needed to be discussed.

"That you can help me with before you leave," Federico conceded. "All of the information you need is at Jacobo's office in Castolón and at his ranch in Santa Elena."

"Speaking of Santa Elena, what will happen to Carmelita, Papá?" Felipe asked.

"We'll let her continue to live on the ranch as long as she wants. She made my son happy. She deserves something."

"Shouldn't we consider selling the ranch? How can you handle both?" Felipe asked.

"It's the only thing we have that still belongs to a Villalba. I will manage. As long as I'm alive, it stays in the family. You can do whatever you want with it after I die."

As it turned out, Carmelita decided to return to her family. She was as independent as her lover and wanted nothing from the Villalbas. She would not tell Jacobo's family of her pregnancy; she would raise her child with her surname since Jacobo never gave her his.

When Carmelita left *Los Fuegos*, it made Federico rethink everything. In a moment of sadness, Federico decided that maybe it was best to sell *Los Fuegos,* terminate his lease and return to Aldama, México as Felipe had suggested.

On January 12, 1931, he responded to Felipe's letter wherein he asked his father once again to consider a move to México. Federico wrote to his son:

> *If it is true that you want me away from here, write to México*
> *and arrange for immediate passage of my stock. I do not want*
> *to be here any longer. I live in fear for my family since your*
> *brother's murder. Please make immediate arrangements with*
> *the Mexican government for the passage of three hundred and*
> *fifty head of cattle, one hundred mares, thirty mules, thirty-five*
> *remuda horses, seven hundred goats, two Ford trucks, Jacobo's*
> *car, four saddles and the household furniture. Do this immedi-*
> *ately as I feel that we are in great danger.*

In the meantime, Santos returned to help his father follow through with his plans. Lico agreed to help, but only as needed. His central focus would continue to be his family and the small herd he and Santos had begun to nurture in a small adjoining spread.

Felipe immediately sent off two letters, one to the Consul General of México in Presidio, Texas, and the other to the senior administrator in Ojinaga, México. Before either official could respond, Federico wrote another letter to tell Felipe that he had changed his mind.

"I realized that I was acting cowardly," he wrote. "No man has ever succeeded in making me do something against my will. It is my desire to remain and let the Anglos know that a Villalba does not run! *Aqui vivo, y aqui muero,* Here I live, and here I die."

The Frontier Era Ends

The political climate in the Big Bend began changing dramatically in 1932, an election year. Roosevelt had become the vanguard for the "forgotten," little guy.

Howard Perry was beginning to feel political pressure from the left. Because of the low wages and his flagrant disregard for labor laws, the mercury industry and the Chisos Mining Company in particular, he was receiving a great deal of notice from the "New Dealers."

Perry knew that he would soon face an onslaught of criticism and possibly even monetary sanctions. He and the other mine owners began circling their political wagons in preparation for a formidable battle that was to come in the form of the National Recovery Act.

Federico in the meantime had his own battles to deal with, not the least of which was trying to overcome the death of his son. Over the coming months, pressure continued to build on him from the strain of trying to manage both his ranch and Jacobo's ranch in Santa Elena. His days were long and hard.

The burden and the extra work began to take its toll on Federico, now seventy-five years old. Felipe's concern for his father's health had indeed been valid. Though spiritually and mentally strong, his physical health continued on a downward spiral. Just after the Christmas holidays, he complained of shortness of breath and dizziness. Try as she would, Severita could not convince her husband to take time out of his hectic daily routine to rest and see a doctor.

As Federico prepared for bed on the evening of January 6, 1933, his tenth wedding anniversary, he fell to the floor clutching his chest and gasping for air. Severita ran to him and cradled his head in her lap. She knew it was a heart attack.

"*Viejo*, don't leave me," she pleaded.

Federico knew he was dying. His blue eyes looked at Severita in anguish. He could not find the breath to speak. He wanted to tell her that he loved her and ask that she say goodbye to his children for him. She saw it all in his eyes before he closed them for the final time. He was tired. It was time to rest. Federico appeared to smile as life left his body.

News of Federico Villalba's death reached all corners of the Big Bend. His life had touched many people. His struggles and victories were legendary. His good friends Roy and Hallie Stillwell were devastated at the news. Later, reminiscing with his wife, Hallie, Roy said, "Fred Villalba was a good man and a good friend.

"Old Fred didn't believe that luck had anything to do with circumstances. He'd always tell me that tomorrow's results, good or bad, were always dictated by today's actions. He never found fault with anyone but himself when things didn't work out. If someone got the better of him, it was because he'd 'allowed it'.

"Didn't mean he wasn't going to deal with you for it—just meant he felt he should never have allowed it to happen in the first place. I'm going to miss the old coot. Hell, the whole damn Big Bend's going to miss old blue eyes!"

No Will
and More Problems

Hunter Metcalfe was now district judge. His former partner Charles Mead contacted him to let him know that Federico Villalba had died. Mead immediately checked with Felipe for a will. As meticulous as Federico had been about his business affairs, he died intestate with no last will and testament. This meant that, even in death, Federico would face a final challenge of legendary proportions.

In 1928, Howard Perry had retained Mead & Metcalfe to represent the Chisos Mining Company in a dispute with the Rainbow Mine, another of the mines Federico had partial interest in. Perry had been caught tunneling into the Rainbow mine's adjacent leasehold, but not before extracting some quarter of a million dollars in cinnabar. The law firm represented him in a lawsuit that followed. Perry wound up paying a legal settlement totaling about $250,000.

Through the course of the litigation, the law firm had cultivated a relationship of sorts with Perry and his right hand man, Robert Cartledge. Perry had been given the impression by Cartledge that Federico owed money to the Chisos and La Harmonía stores. It is the Villalba family's understanding that Cartledge was instructed by Perry, perhaps via Charles Mead to contact Judge Metcalfe and file a petition as a creditor requesting appointment as temporary administrator of Federico's estate.

As soon as they received the nod from Judge Metcalfe, Cartledge immediately began identifying Federico's assets and liquidating his estate to pay his debts. Mead and Metcalfe's motives may have been to distance themselves from any liabilities that were not associated with their holdings, vis-à-vis the ranch. Cartledge, as the Villalbas feared, had his own agenda.

"It was like hiring the fox to guard the henhouse," Felipe was heard to say. Even though the Villalbas felt that the deck was stacked, Felipe immediately complained to the court demanding that they remove Cartledge and appoint him as administrator. It is only speculation, but Felipe's complaint may have been why Cartledge was never directed to formally file a petition to become permanent administrator of Federico's estate. Had he done so, he would have received specific instructions about how to administer the estate and would have been under much greater scrutiny by the courts. As it happened, Felipe's demand never bore fruit and Cartledge was allowed to proceed willy nilly.

The Villalbas gathered for *el entierro*, the burial of their father. Federico had always wanted his final resting place to be on his first ranch. Charles Mead, however, would not allow it. He didn't want the Villalbas to feel as if they had any right to any part of the ranch, even if it was only an interment plot. The family buried Federico in the Terlingua cemetery next to Jacobo.

Cartledge offered to pay for the funeral. The Villalbas thought it was a parting gesture done out of respect for the man. The family later learned that $2,000 in expenses was billed to Federico's estate. This amount didn't even include a tombstone. Felipe later paid for that out of his own pocket.

Cartledge advised the Villalbas that he would divide Federico's cattle, goats and sheep and send them to various ranchers in the area, the most notable of which was Homer Wilson. The intent was to "grow the herds" to help pay off Federico's debts. Once sold, Cartledge would halve the profits with the ranchers. Homer, however, refused to accept any of the proceeds of the sale. He liked and respected Federico. It just seemed like the right thing to do.

Each time Cartledge was asked to give an accounting of the estates debts, he told the Villalba family that the total amount could not yet be tallied. The one debt he'd made clear from the beginning was the monies owed to the Chisos Mining and La Harmonía stores. It totaled about $2,700. These accounts were actually opened for Santos and Lico by their father to help them out. It had been Federico's practice to pay off the accounts each time he would sell stock or wool at shearing time. The Villalbas became suspicious when Cartledge denied that any such payments had been made.

In the ensuing years, Lico and Santos struggled to maintain a respectable herd. Regina and Miguel set up homestead in La Minita. Miguel returned to teaching, supplementing his income with tanning and selling goat hides. By this time, six more children had joined the Esquivel clan; Manuel, born on August 23, 1927, Trinidad, October 25, 1929, Socorro, May 11, 1932, Jacobo, February 18, 1934, and Federico on February 2, 1936. By unfortunate coincidence, Federico was born on *El Dia de La Candelaria*, Candlemas Day. Candlemas is a Christian feast commemorating the purification of the Virgin Mary and the presentation of the infant Jesus in the Temple. Candles are brought to mass to be blessed for use during the year.

Traditionally, children born on this day are given the name Candelario or Candelaria. Regina, however, would have none of that.

"*Sobre mi tomba*, over my grave will my son be given the name Candelario," Regina said. She despised Candelario Baiza for all the pain she felt he'd brought on the family. Being a stickler for religious tradition, Miguel convinced Regina to give their son the controversial name as a middle name, never to be uttered in her presence.

After many failed attempts at persuading Regina to move to México permanently, it was decided that the Esquivel family would relocate to El Paso. In El Paso, Miguel worked for American General Insurance as a salesman. On December 10, 1939, their eighth child, Jesus, was born.

A Final Fight for Dignity

The Villalbas continued their battle with Cartledge who kept insisting that there was no money left in their father's estate, as all had been used to pay off Federico's debts. They reached their limit with "*El Bob*" and hired the law firm of Morriss & Morriss in San Antonio to file a lawsuit against Robert Cartledge. They alleged dereliction and misappropriation of funds in the execution of their father's estate. A jury trial was held in August of 1940.

The jury found that Cartledge had made grievous errors in the handling of the Villalba estate. A judgment was entered in the amount of $4,488.33. Mead & Metcalfe immediately filed a Writ of Error that was denied. The law firm then filed an appeal. The appellate court denied Cartledge's request for rehearing and affirmed the judgment on June 19, 1941, whereupon an appeal to the Texas Supreme Court was filed.

In the interim, Cartledge hired the firm of White, Taylor and Chandler out of Austin to go after Howard Perry to try to recoup some of his money by claiming that the monies credited to the Chisos Mining Store from the sale of Villalba's assets were due him for an alleged personal loan he had made to Federico in the amount of $2,000. He had made a mistake and wanted to find a way of making Perry pay for at least part of it. In answer to a demand letter to Perry from Attorney White on December 11, 1941, Perry wrote:

> *I have been asked time and time again to pay Robert out like you suggest but I have not seen myself clear to do so. I had always believed that I owed it to The Chisos Mining Company not to do so. You see, Robert and Valenzuela [Feliz] who are partners in the cattle business, financed that business with funds of Chisos Mining Company, though my permission was never asked by Robert. I felt that Robert would, of course, let the $3,000 or thereabouts which he loaned the Company* [Cartledge's and Valenzuela's cattle business] *to remain as security for the cattle account, to which he immediately, cheerfully acquiesced and the thing ran along. The Valenzuela account which was of course $7,000 to $8,000 and which never paid us any interest which of course should never have occurred.*

In the same letter he also wrote:

> *After Robert took hold of Billalba* [sic] *matters and the Billalba Estate matters he became kind of a czar. He did not like very much to talk with me about the situation and decidedly not with the Billalba heirs, as he plainly should have.*

By the date of this letter, Cartledge had been absent from the Chisos Mining Company for a year owing to Perry's desire to distance himself from the Villalba brouhaha. After twenty-nine years of service, Perry unceremoniously fired Robert Cartledge.

Perry's problems with Cartledge were symptomatic of bigger troubles. The demand for mercury had dropped to an all-time low. Perry was eventually forced to close the mine in 1946. All of the other mines had been abandoned long before the Chisos closed.

Meanwhile the former sheriff, Everett Townsend, who had been elected Texas State Representative in 1932, coauthored a bill to make a portion of the Big Bend a state park. About 150,000 acres were set aside for park purposes. Robert Cartledge had been recruited by Townsend to work as an auditor with the Texas State Parks Board, an agency whose purpose was to work towards making the entirety of the Big Bend, some 750,000 acres, into a national park. The agency was systematically purchasing land by way of eminent domain, using the power of the government to take property from the few remaining landowners for what the landowners felt was far less than what their land was worth.

Bad news for Cartledge

On December 31, 1941, the Texas Supreme Court denied a motion for rehearing of the Cartledge appeal. The following is an excerpt from the letter Hunter Metcalfe sent to Robert Cartledge, dated January 2, 1942.

The Supreme Court on Wednesday of this week [December 31, 1941] over-ruled motion for rehearing in our appeal in the Billalba [sic] Estate matter; and as you know this means 'taps' for us. This is the end of the row.

There is nothing left except that you should immediately make your plans to comply with the terms of the judgment; and I would advise you to do this without delay and not bring about a condition which would cause additional litigation which will result only in delay and additional expenses....

On January 13, 1942, Cartledge admitted defeat. He took Metcalfe's advice and had the First National Bank issue a draft in the amount of $4,800 to the Villalba heirs.

Ironically, the payout to the Villalba family was rumored to be larger than what the National Park Service paid Howard Perry and Cartledge combined for their Big Bend land. As hard as he tried, Cartledge was never able to recover any money from the Chisos Mining Company.

Perry declared insolvency on October 1, 1942. On June 12, 1944 Big Bend was established as a National Park by Congressional Act.

Federico's good reputation and unimpeachable business dealings turned out to be a crucial factor in the Texas Supreme Court's review of the trial. One could say Federico Villalba won his final battle in the Big Bend, and he did so from the grave.

23

The Villalbas Leave the Big Bend

The remaining Villalbas finally bid a bittersweet farewell to Terlingua. Santos and Lico remained in the Big Bend through the course of the estate litigation, working their small ranch. They, like some of the other ranchers, were paid less than what they felt their land was worth by the National Park Service. Lico and Santos thought of filing a lawsuit on their own as well as other ranchers' behalf.

Felipe convinced them doing so would be costly, time consuming and most likely futile. They took his advice and reluctantly returned to Alpine. Felipe resumed his career in El Paso, and Jorge remained at his farm in Big Spring.

During the litigation, Regina reluctantly accompanied Miguel back to Ocampo, the Esquivel political stronghold. Shortly after their return, Miguel's hopes for the Mexican Senate were dashed when he shot and killed a man in self-defense.

While on a buying trip to a neighboring city to purchase wheat flour for his family, who had never acquired a taste for corn tortillas, Miguel was accosted by a man who was known for hysterical outbursts and for attacking people without warning or any apparent motive. Miguel had reached the outskirts of town when the man, armed with a machete, sprang out from behind a tree and blocked the buckboard.

Miguel recognized the man and yelled, "Get away crazy man!"

The man stood his ground, ranting incoherently and waving the machete at the horse. Miguel pulled his pistol from his waistband and pointed it as the man advanced.

"For the last time get away or I will shoot!" Miguel shouted.

The man suddenly ran to the side of the buckboard and lunged at Miguel, who instinctively pulled the trigger. At such close range, the man's chest exploded with the impact of the bullet, spewing blood over Miguel and the side of the buckboard. The body flailed back, landing in the water and mud, remnants of a thunderstorm from the evening before. Miguel jumped off the buckboard to see if the man was still alive. He was dead. He immediately returned to town and reported the shooting.

After lengthy questioning at the police station and accompanying two *oficiales* to the site of the shooting, Miguel returned home to tell Regina what happened. He told her that charges would not be filed. This did little to calm his wife.

"I want to go back to El Paso," she announced.

"But what of our lives here?" Miguel asked.

"I have no life here and now with you killing that man…" Regina was disturbed to the point of not being able to finish her sentence though her husband knew exactly how she felt.

"We'll talk about this later, when you've calmed down," Miguel said.

"I am leaving for El Paso tomorrow with or without you," Regina declared.

Miguel had heard this determination in her voice before. His wife never made idle threats. He hoped that he could change her mind. Miguel left for their store to gather his wits.

Regina knew Miguel would withhold funds if he thought that would keep her in Ocampo. Regina went to her jewelry box to see what she could sell to finance her trip.

The next morning after Miguel left for the store in the buckboard, Regina packed the minute her husband was through the door.

With children and baggage squeezed into every inch of the *Fordingo's* interior, Regina drove to the pawnshop in town owned by the *Chino* (Chinese man).

The children had taken many trips without their father. They accepted what their mother said and promptly fell asleep.

That evening, Miguel arrived home to find Regina and the children missing. He was not surprised. The next day he resigned his position and left for Ciudad Juárez, the border town across from El Paso. He'd let his visa lapse, thinking he and his family would remain in México. He sent word to Regina of his travel plans. She and the children joined him soon after he arrived, but only because he promised to move them to El Paso as soon as his documents were reinstated. When Regina received her inheritance money, she put a down payment on a home on Manzana Street and bought a washing machine.

Santos and his family lived in Alpine for a time. He eventually moved his family to San José, California. Lico joined his family in El Paso, where they had moved to seek a better life away from the violence and poor social relations that plagued the Big Bend. Jorge remained in Big Spring. For reasons known only to Jorge, he changed the spelling of his surname to Billalba.

Severita went to live with her niece Natividad García de Franco in Pueblo Nuevo outside of Alpine.

Though his name is not worthy of mention, his demise is. "Det" Walker died in Durango, Colorado in a mysterious house fire in 1949 at the age of 55. His family thinks the fire might have been lit by a jilted girlfriend. Maybe it was, and maybe it wasn't.

It had been Federico Villalba's dream, since his youth, to give his family a good life and a bountiful inheritance, and that he did. Today the beauty of the land he loved and worked so hard to maintain is preserved, in large part, in a National Park, perhaps the most beautiful and rugged in the southwest. The remnants of old ranches, corrals, buildings and mines that spot the desert are preserved as monuments to the brave men and women who settled in the Big Bend when it was one of the last frontiers.

Federico Villalba's legacy transcends money, position and politics. He stood for strength and dignity in a time when people of Mexican heritage were treated as inferior and unequal. He passed on to his descendants and to West Texas a legacy that reflects an indomitable spirit that touches and enriches lives even today.

The man that lives with honor and humility is a man that lives forever. – Federico Villalba

ACKNOWLEDGEMENTS

My sincerest thanks to Federico Villalba IV, Sandra Villalba de Soto, Paul Villalba, Clara Rodríguez de Villalba, Santos "Blocker" Villalba, Jr., Alicia Dávila de Villalba and Edward Villalba. Without their friendship, encouragement and participation, this book would never have been possible.

A very special thanks to my cousin, attorney Miguel Villalba, a distinguished criminal defense attorney in El Paso, who collaborated with me in developing the chapters involving the trial of Jorge Villalba for the murder of Winslow Coffman. The transcript of the trial no longer exists; lacking that, I relied on my *primo's* legal expertise, experience and writing skills to help create a fictional account that would capture the essence and tenor of the real trial based on available bits and pieces of actual accounts. Some accounts of the trial came from Kenneth B. Ragsdale, *Big Bend Country—Land of the Unexpected* (Texas A&M University Press, College Station, 1998), and interviews with Santos Villalba, Sr., Santos Villalba, Jr., Jacobo Villalba, Miguel Esquivel G., Regina Villalba de Esquivel and Herminia Villalba-Esquivel de Casas.

Thank you to my cousin Rodolfo Villalba for his assist in providing me with ancient family history.

To María Louisa Franco de Madrid and her mother, Natividad García de Franco, I give my undying gratitude for providing me with wonderful anecdotes and pictures that were entrusted to Maria Louisa and her mother, Natividad, by Severa "Severita" García de Villalba. Her contributions were the icing on the cake.

My thanks to Meletta Bell, senior archivist, Archives of the Big Bend at Sul Ross State University in Alpine, Texas, and her staff for her putting up with my countless e-mails and for providing the Robert Cartledge Papers which were a great help in writing the book.

Many, many thanks to B. J. Gallego, a field representative for Archives of the Big Bend at Sul Ross, for his invaluable assistance, well appreciated friendship and for opening up so many friendly doors.

Muchisimas gracias to Leo Dominguez, vice president of Advancement and University Relations at Sul Ross, for his continual support and encouragement.

I am grateful to historian Glenn Willeford for his assistance. His willingness to share resources, including a profound knowledge of both the Texas Big Bend and of La Frontera de Chihuahua, as well as his authorial skills, lent much to the successful completion of the work. Willeford's latest full-length works include *Cemeteries and Funerary Practices in the Big Bend of Texas, 1850 to the Present* (2006) and *Dirty Cop? The Rise and Fall of a Texas Sheriff, Memoir & Essays* (2008).

My appreciation to John Klingemann Franco, PhD student at the University of Arizona, for sharing his knowledge of Mexican history and Pancho Villa.

To my sister, María Theresa Casas de Elizalde, my thanks for allowing me the privilege of finishing what she was unable to complete because of health problems. She was the first of my siblings to travel to the Big Bend to do research with the hope of writing a book about our great-grandfather.

Other sources include Arthur R. Gómez, *A Most Singular Country*, (Brigham Young University), Charles Redd Center for Western Studies, 1990); Laura Villegas, *Big Bend's Hispanic Heritage*, (Texas National History); Glenn P. Willeford, *Mexican Settlers in the Big Bend Region 1889-1945*, (An oral presentation for La Semana de Humanismo La Universidad Autónoma de

Chihuahua, Facultad de Filosofía y Letras, presented by the author on November 6, 2001 at La Quinta Gameros); *Fulminic Acid*, (The 1911 Edition of *Love to Know* Encyclopedia. The Handbook of Texas Online, University of Texas at Austin; *The Black Seminoles*, Kenneth Porter, revised and edited by Alcione M. Amos and Thomas P. Senter, (University Press of Florida, 1996); *The 1918 Influenza Pandemic*, Molly Billings, (Stanford University Press, 1997); *La Harmonía Company Store*, Castolón, (National Park Service official NPS Website); *Prohibition in the Big Bend* (Texas History.com); Kenneth B. Ragsdale, *Quicksilver–Terlingua & the Chisos Mining Company* (Texas A&M University Press, College Station, 1976); W. D. Smithers, *Chronicles of the Big Bend–a Photographic Memoir of Life on the Border*, (Texas State Historical Association, 1999); Charles H. Harris III and Louis R. Sadler, *Texas Rangers and the Mexican Revolution–The Bloodiest Decade, 1910-1920* (University of New Mexico Press, 2004); Trial records, Cause No. 1077 & 1078, *The State of Texas vs. George Billalba*, County District Court, Alpine Texas: *The Alpine Avalanche*, May 31, 1923; *El Paso Times*, May 27, 1923; *El Paso Herald*, May 18, 1933. Clifford B. Casey, *Soldiers, Ranchers and Miners in the Big Bend*; (Big Bend National Park, Texas, Division of History, Office of Archeology and Historic Preservation); *Imaginary Kingdom: Texas as seen by the Rivera and Rubi military expeditions, 1727 and 1767*, edited and with an introduction by Jack Jackson, with annotations by William C. Foster (Texas State Historical Association, 1995).

Hats off to editors extraordinaire Loretta Hudson and Roy Hamric for their significant contribution to making this book a good "right side of the brain" experience.

Most of all, my love and thanks to my wife, Arlene, who endured my countless hours away from her, at all hours of the day and night, while I researched and wrote the book.